FLIPPING
THE
BIRD

MARGARITA MEYENDORFF

DEDICATION

I dedicate this book
to all who dare to push the envelope…

CONTENTS

INTRODUCTION

Readers of Margarita Meyendorff (Mourka)'s memoir *DP Displaced Person* will be further entertained and engrossed by this varied collection. The little girl we met in *DP*, who began life in a DP camp in Germany and spent her childhood in a Russian émigré enclave in Nyack, New York, follows up with an anthology of thirty short pieces and one extraordinary screenplay—stories of defiance and impudence in the face of injustice, both public and private.

Here, she always maintains her insouciance, a charm that helps her survive even such dire circumstances as being detained by Serbian officers during war, and as lighthearted as slipping backstage for private time with Rudolph Nureyev. Her tales always surprise and delight, and often move us with their depth of feeling. This collection is steeped in her

Russian background, and she serves up a *zakuska* of flavorful memories–all spiced with her spirit. Early stories show her escape from the stifling sickroom her parents inhabited–Mourka rebelled by driving fast with dangerous boyfriends and finally fled home with potato soup on her shoes.

On her own as a young girl in the world of big-city and then regional theaters, she tells tales of outrageous jobs as a go girl, wrapped in tin foil. Many stories are hilarious; some skirt danger. She recounts her sensual adventures, forays against prudery. In a preview of the Me-Too movement, Mourka also combats sexual harassment and unfair treatment on several jobs. She fights the rigidity of the establishment in various forms, defying the FBI and, on other occasions, shocking the locals of her small town by appearing topless at the neighborhood pool and also performing costumed only in a Soviet flag.

Along the way, we meet a woman trapped and rightly angered by her first husband, who leaves her alone to care for her first baby *("Shine")*. In the title story, "Flipping the Bird," Mourka defies an unfair school administrator and, yes, flips him the bird. Feisty as she is, Mourka's war against injustice is never rancorous. Her generosity and uplifting nature always triumph. In her infinite variety, we see Mourka in contrasting moods and modes, gentle and loving with her second husband and, significantly, defying death itself to have a poignant reunion with her long-gone mother in "Rendezvous." You will find yourself doubled over with laughter at her fury at being locked in a "Car Wash" and moved to tears by her most serious stories. Endlessly inventive, Mourka's talent shines in multicolored reflections. Her personal essays, plays, and screenplay shimmer with the iridescence of the peacock feather pictured on the cover.

Laura Shaine Cunningham, author of the memoirs *Sleeping Arrangements* and *A Place in the Country*

PRECIS

All lives have themes that run through them like ribbons, motifs that reoccur. As I reviewed my own past to write these pieces, I could see that my theme was rebellion, sometimes as lighthearted resistance, more often as true defiance against injustice. I always fought whoever and whatever I found oppressive. As a free spirit, I defied convention. There is more than one tale in which I go topless. I could not be confined by senseless restrictions.

It would seem that I am often angry but in fact I would say I am forever free. I am not a screaming hysterical woman; I spare my voice, which is trained for singing and projection on the stage. I admit my exits have a certain theatrical flair.

How often have I "flipped the bird?" You will find out in this chronicle. We all know the expression.

Perhaps you, too, have given "the finger" to someone who has offended you. I feel certain everyone has wanted to! When I look back, I see I was born in defiance of the times, in the aftermath of the Second World War, at a time when it took some extra emotion to produce a child in a displaced persons camp in Germany.

My parents were aristocrats turned into refugees, and their one great action of defiance was to flee Russia and Estonia and cross Nazi Germany to find temporary shelter in a DP camp and then complete their journey to longed-for freedom in America. The story of my early life is told in my memoir, *DP Displaced Person.* In that book, I was the three-year-old girl sitting in a wagon, an imperious little baroness who commanded her beloved redheaded little boy cousin, "Pull me!" That willfulness remained and was potentially seeded with more temper had this dear boy refused. We may have resided in refugee quarters in former elephant stalls, but regal manner and command were still in my bloodline.

By the time I knew my parents, as a child, all I could see was they had the fight knocked out of them— my father an invalid, lying on a makeshift sofa bed, holding his "stomick" and groaning, and my mother, the former beauty weeping into the sink of dirty dishes after a day in a sweatshop.

Later, I could conjure from photos and letters the wildly attractive, passionate couple they had been. Theirs had been a post-youth union, my mother previously married with two sons, my father the dashing bachelor Baron, who had been a royal White cadet, close to the last tsar, Nicholas II; he had danced with Anastasia. It was fitting that my mother and father met in disguise—at a masquerade party. I see the pictures of my pretty Marie Antoinette mother and my dashing masked father and try to match them to the defeated parents who had almost given up raising me. Growing up, I couldn't see beyond the wreckage.

It was no wonder I rebelled against them both, from the miasma which engulfed our tiny, camphor-scented dusty little apartment. Their dashed dreams would not suffocate my hopes. I ran for forbidden romance; I raced at illegal speeds. I had, to my mind, a wonderful time!

Now, it is a more reflective person who looks back and examines the nature of resistance and why and how and when I chose to flip the bird, actually or metaphorically. And I see that, in the end, I address the mysteries in my life, in every life, and defy even time, fate, and death. Venting my anger, my frustration, fighting injustice gave ballast to my life and propelled me through a miserable marriage and much adversity to the life, creative work, and marriage I enjoy so much today.

You'll see. I welcome you with my open embrace. No finger. Not at you, dear reader. Only toward the antagonists who may well also anger you. The past informs the future. For everyone. For you. One of the best theatrical plays and titles ever is *Look Back in Anger*. Do so and you may find, as I have, that your anger frees you to experience self-respect and joy.

PART ONE:

THE PASSION
OF DEFECTION

To rebel, one must defy someone or something. I think those of us who do rebel begin resistance against our first authority figures, our parents, the background that molded them, and by extension, ourselves.

For me, that background was my Russian heritage, which, from the start, exerted and still does a push/pull on my deepest feelings. While I love the culture, the music, the dance, the poetry, language, and literature, I also fought the restrictions of Russian Orthodoxy and the protocols of aristocracy, at least as handed down by my father the Baron. You will see soon enough how the tempestuous girl I was (who still lives within me) had to fight hard to save herself.

The force to break free, to be myself had to be near violent and, in fact, provoked equal and opposite reactions in my parents. As a passionate teenage girl, I crept back home one night to be greeted by my father pointing a shotgun. He didn't shoot but the war was declared. And it was a war I had to win, or my spirit would wither, and my true self die, shot down like the many game birds my father took for sport while hunting on the family estate back in Estonia.

ARISTOCRATS DON'T DANCE

My father, a Baron down to his fine bones, often admonished me: "Aristocrats don't dance." By that, he did not mean *all* dancing. Oh, *no*, aristocrats certainly *did* dance—in endless elegant balls. They waltzed their way through the Romanov Dynasty, three hundred years of box steps and a promenade right up to the Russian Revolution.

The last Tsar, Nicholas II, and the Tsarina Alexandra held glorious costume extravaganzas. The final great Imperial Ball was held in 1903, which brought forth most of Russia's highest nobles and royals in fantastic seventeenth-century dress. Photos remain of the great beauties such as Zinaida Yusupova, looking devastating in their *kokoshnik* headdresses and gold-threaded gowns. My own great forebear, Baron Meyendorff, appeared in a full suit of armor, complete with chain mail and a pickelhaube spike-pointed helmet.

The famous photograph of Nicholas and Alexandra presiding from their thrones shows us a passive Nicholas looking pleased and Tsarina Alexandra distinctly pained. She was known to be private and would have preferred a life of seclusion.

I like to think she might have liked to "flip the bird" at the excessive delirious occasion and retreated to her royal bed.

What my father meant by "Aristocrats don't dance" was that they did not dance professionally, for hire. To be a dancer or an actress was regarded as *risqué*, and dancing for pay, on a stage, was for concubines and mistresses. Even the classical ballet was a province exploited by titled and wealthy men, the prime resource for finding their graceful fetching young mistresses.

Nicholas himself had his first sexual affair with the petite ballerina beauty Mathilde Kschessinka. Of course, he would never have considered marrying her; respectability and, to be fair, a deeper love, were reserved for his dear cousin Alix, whose chaste romance ran parallel with the naughtier pas de deux her future husband was enjoying with the little ballerina.

Did my father once indulge in such affairs with dancers? If he did, he never confided in me. But he was adamant that I must never dance for hire or on the stage, and of course, my desire to do so grew in great leaps, *grand jetes* of rebellion. "*Аристократы не танцуют*…Aristocrats don't dance," my father said to me. "Aristocrats play the piano and become concert pianists."

"But I don't want to play the piano, I want to dance. Please let me dance!"

In December of 1949, my family and I immigrated to the United States from a displaced persons camp in Germany. I was two years old. We were Russians—my father believed that the monarchy in Russia would someday rise up again, that his possessions and property, the estate in Kumna, the mansion in St. Petersburg would be returned, that it was just a matter of time. In the meantime, the family would live in America, on the edge of poverty, maintaining an aristocratic existence in a two-room, cluttered flat in Nyack, New York.

My pleas fell on deaf ears.

At age six, I was passionate about dance. I wanted to become a ballerina—to wear a tutu, the tights, the fabulous costumes. I wanted to move my six-year-old long-legged body like the swans in a film version of Tchaikovsky's *Swan Lake,* which I saw projected on a wall in somebody's house in Nyack. At age six, I didn't have to be the main swan…just a swan. I wanted to dance across a huge stage, dressed in a white diaphanous skirt that showed off my white tights and my white satin ballet slippers and have one of those gorgeous male dancers select me from all the swans and dance a pas de deux.

My dream of becoming a ballerina was not that far-fetched. My best friend, Mika, who was five years old, was already taking ballet lessons from Larissa Georgiovna, a Russian émigré dance diva transplanted to Nyack from Moscow. Like many émigrés, she had been an acclaimed principal ballet dancer at one of the best ballet troupes in Moscow and was now forced to make ends meet in a new country by teaching dance to Russian immigrant children.

Even in her seventies, Larissa was still beautiful. She had long white hair, partly swept up in combs and the rest dangling down to her waist. She always wore makeup, emphasizing her deep-brown eyes and eyebrows, and she wore dark red lipstick. She looked as if she was always ready to step out on stage.

I accompanied my friend Mika to many of her dance classes, and I would sit watching, mesmerized by Larissa's graceful movements as she demonstrated ballet steps, ballet barre techniques, and "across the floor" ballet movements. When I came home, I would beg my parents to let me take ballet classes from Larissa Georgiovna.

My father, ever the disciplinarian, forced me to play the piano. He would hold a ruler over my fingers and hit them if I played a wrong note.

My love for dance continued into the late 1950s, when Rita Moreno stunned New York audiences with her wild Latina dancing in the Broadway production of *West Side Story*. I learned the songs, acted out the speeches, and choreographed the dances, all in the confines of my bedroom. Jumping from bed to bed, from chair to chair, I would make faces in the mirror, using my makeshift closet as a dressing room, and create my own theatrical and musical fantasy. I was ten years old.

During my teenage years, my rebellious spirit kicked in when black kids in my high school introduced me to dancing to soul, R & B, jazz, and the blues. It was the '60s, with race riots and civil rights marches raging in the nation, and frowned upon for white kids to dance with black kids. More than once I was removed from the high school dance floor for dancing provocatively with my black friends. When most of the kids in school were dancing to bubble gum music on WABC, I was dancing to Nina Simone, Ray Charles, and Otis Redding and listening to Symphony Sid, all-night jazz radio. I felt the music deep in my bones, and although it wasn't classical ballet music, my body naturally moved to the sway of jazz, soul, and blues. I was hooked.

My father still couldn't let go of his piano dream.

I was musically talented and played the piano until I was sixteen years old. One evening, during a recital at my piano teacher's house, I was in the middle of playing a Chopin prelude when my father, who sat in the third row, turned up his hearing aid so high that a piercing sound screeched through the room in shrill disharmony to the Chopin piece that I was playing. For half a second, I stopped playing, knowing full well where that awful sound was coming from. I finished playing, stood up, walked out of the recital room, and never touched the piano again.

I was nineteen years old when I made the decision to leave Nyack, move in with my cousin in New York City, and pursue a theatrical and dance career. When I told my mother of my decision, she was so distraught she threw a whole bowl of soup at me. My father's piano dream was vanquished, and I left home with potato soup on my shoes.

In New York City, I began taking dance classes at the famous Luigi's Jazz Dance Center in mid-Manhattan. I had no time to lose. I took classes almost every day, often walking from my various jobs or from my apartment on Eighty-Eighth St. and Broadway to save money on transportation. Despite the fact that, at age twenty-one, he had suffered paralyzing injuries in a car accident, Luigi was a fabulous teacher and choreographer, who created his own "feeling from the inside—never stop moving" ballet-based dance technique. I never stopped moving and pushed myself to the max.

To enhance my jazz technique, I took classes at the Harkness School of Ballet. I killed my hips to turn out at just the right angle, hoping that my Russian genes would work in my favor—after all, aren't the Russians masters of the ballet technique? And what about their work ethic—could it not rub off on me? But when I attempted an arabesque, the ballet teacher started hitting me with a stick because my leg was not high enough, I quit. The blow from the stick felt too much like my father's ruler striking my fingers over the piano.

For the next fifteen years, a series of events blew me sideways, and I let my dance dreams slip away—I fell in love, married, moved to the Hudson Valley, had two children, and…divorced. I fell into a low-grade depression, going through my necessary routine as a mother of small children. I did not dance but drooped like a wounded swan.

Then one day, during an ordinary afternoon of shopping for me and my two children as I parked the car near the grocery store and walked down the street with the kids in tow, I stopped in my tracks. I heard music coming from the second floor above the local gift store. It sounded like a combination of African and Hispanic music, with a rhythm that enticed me. I pulled my children into the building and dragged them up the stairs. The music intensified, arousing familiar sensations from an earlier time. I heard that irresistible beat. At the top of the stairs, holding both of my children's hands, my legs like weights, I stared at dancers springing across the floor, moving their arms, shoulders, hips, and legs to Afro-Cuban music. I watched, tears rolling down my face. *How long had it been since I danced so freely, with abandon, to music that stirred my soul?*

Within a week, I donned jazz shoes and tights and went to New York City to class. I spent weekends in New York taking three classes a day—Luigi's, Alvin Ailey Dance School, and Milton Myers Modern Class. At first, my muscles burned; my bones ached. My body hurt so much I could hardly get off the bus and hurry home to my bathtub to soak in Epsom salts. Little by little, class by class, memory muscles at work, my body became stronger, and I was able to keep up with the dancers in the front row. It wasn't ballet but I was dancing—dancing to classical, modern, jazz music, live drumming, music that stirred my passion for dance.

I danced across the floors of studios and performance spaces in New York City and in the Hudson Valley. I danced in *piazzas* in Italy and on the Charles Bridge in Prague. What I lacked in ballet technique, I made up with spirit, stage presence, and my love of dance.

Then one day when I was thirty-five years old and sitting in an airplane seat next to my dancer friend— we were returning home from a performance in Prague—I acknowledged a truth. Without sadness or remorse, I knew that my professional dance days were over, that I had come to an end of an era.

"I need to move on," I told my friend. "I've come to the end of what my dance body can do on stage."

Within six months, I auditioned for a local play and landed the part of Sheila in *The Boys Next Door* by Tom Griffin. I reinvented myself and launched my theatrical career.

I continue to dance. I dance African dance—less taxing on the body than modern or jazz. I love the intricate movements from Guinea, Senegal, Ivory Coast, and the Congo, and the classes are always accompanied by live drummers. These sessions give me energy. As the drums beat a primitive rhythm, they remind me that life need not be complicated.

If my father had allowed me to follow my dreams, would I have danced with Nureyev? Would I have wowed the world with my arabesques and hundreds of ballet turns. *Who knows?*

"Aristocrats don't dance," my father had said, and life for me became a complex and interesting choreography.

THE CHEWING GUM REBELLION

Performed by Mourka for Read650 on 5/3/15
at the Cell Theatre in New York City

The "Aristocrats Don't..." series actually started early when I was just a child.

It emerged early that "aristocrats don't chew gum." And no one rebels as fiercely and secretly as a child.

I am six years old and obsessed with chewing gum. Gum is a forbidden substance. My parents don't allow me to chew it. Maybe chewing gum is not an aristocratic thing to do and we are aristocrats. Maybe it's an American custom and we are Russian, and Russians don't chew gum. I don't know. All I know is that I am a Russian aristocrat, and for this little Baroness, chewing gum is as desirable as it is forbidden.

I start out with stealing gum from the grocery store on the corner of Main Street and Franklin in Nyack, where my parents do their weekly shopping. I love Bazooka the best. It's big in the mouth and I love the pink color, the sugary texture, and the colorful comics that go with the label. I can't read the comics as I don't read English yet, but I love the pictures. I steal the gum, bring it home, hide it under my pillow in my bed, and chew it after my father and I recite the Russian Orthodox night prayer in church Slavonic: "Heavenly King, Comforter, Spirit of Truth, Who art everywhere and fulfilling all the treasure of good and Giver of life. Come and abide in me and cleanse me from all evil … Save me."

Sometimes I fall asleep chewing gum and find the wad next to me in the morning—a big, pink, cold lump of goo. I promptly put the wad back in my mouth, chew it a little, drain all the sugar out, climb out of bed, and finally spit it into the toilet and flush. All traces gone.

Inevitably I am caught stealing the gum. We are in the store, and I swipe the gum and hold it in my pockets—one pack in each pocket. My hands in my pockets for so long rouses my parents' suspicions, and finally they ask me to take my hands out of my pockets and show them everything I have… I am so ashamed. My parents escort me to the checkout lady. With the Bazooka in my hand and in broken English, I have to confess to the cashier that I have taken the gum without paying for it. Nothing like this has ever happened. I have shamed my parents, all Russians, disgraced the aristocracy. I have blasphemed the Eastern Orthodox God, who will now refuse to save me. I apologize and tell everyone standing around in my heavily accented English, "I vill never steal gum again." And I don't.

I graduate from stealing gum to scraping up old gum from the sidewalk, putting it in my mouth, and chewing it. I enjoy the vestiges of mintiness and the sweetness that remain. Some of the pieces have a little gravel or dust stuck to them. No matter, it is gum and I love it. Chewing sidewalk gum goes on for a while, until finally, I get an abscess on my lip. The abscess is like a large pimple that grows and grows. No one has a clue where this pimple has come from, but I have my suspicions—my punishment has begun.

In the future, whenever I am offered gum, even when someone tempts me with a demonstration of a snap and a crackle and a surreal expanding, big, bright bubble of neon-pink Bazooka, my answer is vehement: "No thanks!" Russian aristocracy notwithstanding, I have chewed my last. But my rebellion had just begun, hidden sometimes, like a partisan. At other times, in full revolt.

RUDOLF NUREYEV

As performed by Mourka for Read650 on 4/24/16
at the Cell in New York City

It was 1961, and I was entering puberty and madly, miserably in love with Rudolf Nureyev. I saw us as soul mates and rebels. We had so much in common: He was a peasant from Siberia who had leapt to fame with the Kirov Ballet and defected at the airport in Paris. I was fourteen, an immigrant rebelling against my parents in Nyack, New York. I, too, wanted to defect. Yet what were the chances we would ever meet? The thought that Nureyev would never know me made me weep, even as I gazed at the poster of him flying past in the grandest of jetés.

I was thirteen, when Nureyev defected at Bourget Airport in Paris while on a European tour and overnight became an international sensation. I knew about Nureyev because my friend Mika had a full-sized poster of him tacked to her wall in her bedroom. He was beyond handsome with his high Siberian/near-Tatar cheekbones, full lips, and arching muscled thighs. Mika and I would sit in front of the poster and for hours allow our fantasies about dancing with Nureyev to spin out of control.

Mika's parents (also Russian émigrés) bought tickets to see Nureyev at the Metropolitan Opera in New York City. I tied myself to the piano and promised my own parents years of practice if they would just let me go to the show with Mika. By some God-given miracle, my father acquiesced.

The date arrived. I was going to see Nureyev in *The Nutcracker* at the Met. We took our seats and, along with hundreds of people in the audience, were soon mesmerized by Nureyev's leaps, his catlike movements, and his sensual pas de deux, which surpassed even my highest expectations. He was beyond human. He was feline, sexual... those arched thighs, those full lips, those high cheekbones... I had to get closer, not only to Nureyev but to being a star.

I was not without credits: When I was seven years old, I had performed as a rooster, complete with a huge, red-feathered tail that swung as I moved. I had appeared front and center in a Russian Christmas play on a stage in New York City and sung the Russian equivalent of "cock a doodle doo" (*Ky Ka Pu Ky*) that had to conclude in a high C. I looked down at the front row, at five black-bearded Russian priests. They scared me, made me feel I would fail. I hit the high note anyway. The Russian Orthodox priests' mouths flew open in a collective gasp, a minute pause, and then, the concert hall burst out in applause and cheers. I stood there, resplendent in my red and gold feathers, my plumy tail erect. I basked in the applause; the clapping went on and on. In that moment, I felt loved. Loved for hitting the right note, loved without reservation. Like Nureyev, I was swept up in the moment and, in a sense, never left. We were right for each other and it was only a matter of time.

At *The Nutcracker* curtain call, the audience, in mad abandon, jumped to their feet. During the pandemonium, Mika grabbed my arm, and we ran and ducked behind the curtain and found ourselves backstage in the midst of fantasyland—snowflake ballerinas, uniformed soldiers, fairies, mice, Russian, Chinese, Arab, and Spanish dancers... Speaking in Russian, we pretended that we belonged.

A dancer in harlequin tights led us to Nureyev's dressing room. After what seemed an eternity, Nureyev emerged, as magnificent as on stage. His catlike eyes looked into mine; those sensuous lips spoke—to me. We exchanged some breathless pleasantries in Russian.

"*Какие вы прекрасные!*" (How magnificent you are), he said…

Nureyev seemed thrilled to meet two fourteen-year-old girls and invited us to accompany him to his limousine. As we left by the stage door, the three of us were greeted by a crowd waiting to get a glimpse of him. Mika and I were the blessed. I had him by the right arm and Mika by the left. Before disappearing into his limousine, Nureyev leaned over and kissed each of us on the cheek. My cheek burned with the imprint of his lips and I was branded forever with the promise of a blazing future: Romance, stardom, love would all be mine.

ANDRE AND HIS FATHER-
FIRST LOVE, FIRST FURY

I was twelve years old when I fell in love with nineteen-year-old André. He was tall, handsome, with dark wavy hair and green eyes. He was smart—spoke English, Russian, French, and Polish—and was a student at one of the universities in New York City. I met him when he occasionally visited his parents in Astoria and would sit in on the dinners and the bridge games with my parents. During the 1950s, my parents and I would often drive from Nyack, New York, to Astoria, Queens, where Uncle Vladimir, Aunt Irina, and André had settled. There, dinner was served—*zakuska*—Russian hors d'oeuvres to go with the vodka, followed by a main meat dish served with potatoes and a vinaigrette, a Russian salad. Then, the many desserts were nibbled and tea imbibed, until the bridge games ended, usually in the wee hours of the morning.

While the bridge game was played for hours, I lounged in the adjacent room in TV bliss. Not having a TV at home, I watched show after show until my parents bundled me up and put me half-asleep into the car for the ride home.

The presence of André changed everything. Suddenly, the TV shows became less interesting as I became more enamored with sitting on André's lap while he concentrated on the bridge game. To him, I was a little girl he could tease, like a little sister. To me, he was my first love.

André was the son of Uncle Vladimir and Aunt Irina Von Daroff. Although we were not biologically related, I called Vladimir and Irina *aunt* and *uncle* and loved them as much as if they were dear, close relatives. Uncle Vladimir had been a famous opera singer in Russia. Vladimir was tall, and although, when I knew him, he was almost bald, it was obvious that he had once been a very handsome man with great stage presence. I loved his flamboyance when he played the piano and sang arias from famous operas. His wife, Aunt Irina, was a stunning Polish woman who loved long-haired black cats; they had lived in St. Petersburg, been transplanted to New York City, and were friends of my parents and avid bridge partners.

Uncle Vladimir and my father had been White Russian Army cadets back in Russia. As young men they attended the same academy of the White Russian Cadet Corps, which was located on First Line Street on Vasilyevsky Island across the canal from my father's home in St. Petersburg. St. Petersburg was and still is called the Venice of Russia because of the Neva River and the many waterways and canals and the famous bridges that traverse them.

It cannot be overemphasized the importance of the academy and the connection it forged between my father and Andre's father, Vladimir. Boys entered the academy between the ages of nine and fifteen, and they composed the elite of Russian society, many of them titled like my father, Baron George Meyendorff. The White Russian cadet graduates fought with the Imperial White Russian Army. After the revolution and the Romanov executions, they battled under the White Army in the Russian Civil War.

The White Army fought hard but lost the war, and the survivors either escaped Russia or were sentenced to punitive exile in the Soviet Gulag or outright shot and killed. The bond between Vladimir and my father was one of brothers, survivors. According to Alexandr

Solzhenitsyn, fifteen years after the revolution, not a single White Russian cadet survived inside Russia.

As a child growing up in the Russian émigré enclave in Nyack, New York, I heard many stories in our tiny apartment about how my family and their friends and relatives fled their grand homes and estates in Russia, fleeing from the Bolsheviks after the 1917 Revolution. In 1917, when the Bolshevik Revolution broke out in St. Petersburg before the Bolsheviks seized the Winter Palace, Uncle Vladimir and Aunt Irina boarded one of the last trains heading west toward the Polish border in hopes of avoiding living under communist rule and possible arrest and death. It was several days into the train trip when a raging forest fire appeared on both sides of the tracks. The train had to either speed through the flames or wait until the tracks were passable, the latter not really an alternative as time was of the essence. Uncle Vladimir and Aunt Irina lay down on the floor of their train car, hardly breathing from the smoke and the heat and praying that the train would not be swallowed up by the fire, melted down, and turning them to charred corpses.

Uncle Vladimir and Aunt Irina managed to escape to Poland, and from there they found their way to Paris, where André, their son, was born. In 1953, the

Von Daroff family boarded an airplane bound for New York. On that flight to the United States, Uncle Vladimir wrote a beautiful Russian song entitled *Апельсины*, "Oranges," which I heard him sing many times at numerous Russian gatherings. At such times, everyone wept, the song evoking all our longings. I remember the first line: *Fly, fly, toy airplane and bring my little son to a land where there are no wars, and where oranges grow freely in groves.*

These songs and stories were history lessons for me and imprinted themselves on my young imagination. I never forgot I, too, was Russian, and I had lost my birthright, a grand house in St. Petersburg and a large country estate in Estonia. Here, in the United States, my father became a broken, ill man who designed rugs and needlepoint chair seats for a handicraft shop on Madison Avenue in New York City.

Once, he had been a magnificent horseman, a Baron who was close to the Imperial family, Tsar Nicholas II, and the Tsarina Alexandra. He had even danced with the Grand Duchess Anastasia. When he played bridge with Vladimir, their rarified past as White Cadets hovered over the table, like steam from the ever-boiling samovar—now a teakettle on an electric stove. They were the lucky ones who had survived, but they were also out of place in their new world; the past was more appealing to them than the present. No wonder they clung to it and to one another.

There were annual reunions of the St. Petersburg White Russian Cadet Corps where the cadets who survived the 1917 Revolution and WWII and who were able to immigrate to the United States would get together and party. Most of these reunions were held at the expansive Bogdanovich "dacha" in Carmel, New York, another White Russian enclave centered around a Russian Orthodox monastery in Mahopac, New York. A few times, my parents hosted the reunions at our humble home in Nyack, New York.

André would also attend these reunions, and starry-eyed, I would follow him around while he continued to treat me like a little girl—someone he could manipulate and enjoy playing mock torture games with. Once, he hung me upside down on a huge rock in the woods at the Bogdanovich's. He chased me in the woods until I would fall down exhausted and leave me lying there. He beat me regularly at canasta games and would laugh at my losses. At the time, I wondered if he had a bit of a cruel streak, but this did not stop my infatuation. I craved his attention no matter how badly he treated me.

At fifteen, I started singing lessons with Uncle Vladimir in their apartment in Astoria, until one day, he turned from the piano, stood up, and kissed me on the mouth. Uncle Vladimir knew that I was crazy about his son. *Was he jealous of André?* I was shocked and felt violated. I pushed him away. I told no one, because how could I be an obstacle in my parents' friendship with the Von Daroffs, which was steeped in so much history? I stopped the singing lessons.

André was not aware of how much I adored him. I kept his photo in my wallet. During the time that André served in the US Army, there was a pop tune called "Soldier Boy," which was made popular by The Shirelles. I bought the single forty-five record and would play it and sing with The Shirelles over and over for days, months, even years. I wrote him letters. He never answered.

But this was not to be the end of André but the beginning of a series of disasters that would culminate with his surprise and shocking return. I was to review my childish crush and his behavior through a new lens and at last recognize what had been hidden in that earlier time.

DRIVING WITH THE BARON

In one arena, my rebellion became complicit with my father's subterfuge. My father, Baron George Meyendorff, had never driven an automobile until he immigrated to America at age fifty-five in December of 1949. Soon after our family settled into the renovated elephant stalls at the Clarkstown Country Club in Nyack, New York, it became apparent to him the necessity of driving and owning a car in the American suburbs. I don't know how he managed to get a New York State driver's license with his heavy Russian accent and lack of fluency in English, but the Department of Motor Vehicles did grant him one. For Papa, driving an automobile was the first step toward independence in this new country. Not only was driving a necessity, but the sense of being in command fed into my father's memories of his dashing former life as a Russian baron, when he rode fine steeds in steeplechase races, trained horses to jump and English setters to hunt—a life that had vanished from his reality. But there were problems, and he required an accomplice to a few of his illegal moves.

When I was a little girl, Papa often took me with him on his drives to the city to sell his canvas designs at Rosetta Larson Needlepoint Design on Madison Avenue. He needed a decoy in case he ran into any traffic problems, which was often. I was delighted—it meant I could skip school.

It was on the way to New York City that we approached the toll booth to the George Washington Bridge. Papa noticed that there was no actual person in the toll booth to take his twenty-five cents, the cost to cross the bridge at that time. Instead there was a dish-like receptacle into which one had to throw the money. In Russian, he said, *"Где человек? Да чёрт с ними!"* (No person? The hell with them!)

Papa drove through and all hell broke loose. Bells and sirens went off. I looked back as the toll takers from the manned booths were running after us. My father stopped the car. I slid down under the dashboard—I was petrified that we would be taken to jail.

Papa yelled to me, *"Начинай реветь!"* (Start crying!) And I did. It was my first lesson in Konstantin

Stanislavsky's approach to method acting. The policeman looked under the dashboard at me crying, asked for the toll, and let us go. After that, my father became very adept at throwing the coins into the dish—but he did it in anger. For him, it was like throwing away money—money that he needed.

When I turned sixteen, I got my junior permit, which allowed a great deal of independence. *Almost*. What stood between me and my freedom was the begging. Papa enjoyed this last vestige of control. He knew how badly I wanted to drive his car. I would plead and he would answer, "***Категорически Нет!***" (Categorically *NYET!*)—his favorite phrase.

Begging to use the car became a game that I learned to play with fictitious ploys.

I made up elaborate stories with invented destinations, companions, events. I would use any ruse to escape our gloomy apartment. One tactic that consistently worked with my father was to instruct my best friend, a local Nyack girl, Julie, to ask for the car—in perfect Russian.

"*Можно нам пожалуиста машину сегодня?*" (May we please have the car today?)

We practiced for days until she got it right. Papa found this so amusing that he softened and handed over the keys.

I didn't like driving with my father. He was a terrible driver. Papa avoided using the brakes because he thought he would wear them out. He didn't like to engage the clutch because it would exhaust the gears. At the gas stations, it was always, "Check ze oil, check ze tires, check engine, clean front vindow, clean back window, von dollar gas, pleez."

One day, my parents were driving into town. Papa failed to use the brakes, went through a red light, and plowed into a semi-trailer truck. The car was totaled, but my parents survived, unharmed, a miracle. The Baron's steed was dead, his independence was clipped forever, and he never drove again.

My father didn't drive, but oh, how I did. Fueled by anger, excitement, desire, I found my outlet—drag racing. And soon I hit one hundred m.p.h.

RACING

It was two a.m. on a steamy summer night when my boyfriend, Joe, and I pulled off onto the paved shoulder of the Garden State Parkway. Several young men were leaning on their chrome-glistening hot drag-racing cars, laughing, joking, smoking cigarettes, hanging out—they were waiting for us. We pulled up alongside their fine machines, our car blasting heat and trembling with the vibration of its engine.

"What's up with the girl?" I heard one of the men say.

"She's racing tonight," Joe answered.

My heart skipped a beat.

Joe did have the finest, the hottest, the sexiest 1963 white Chevrolet with a 427 V8 turbo-fired engine—no grill. The front of the car looked like a hungry mouth waiting to cruise the fast quarter-mile straight stretch on the Garden State Parkway extension. Joe's Chevy was fast, and everybody knew it. But with "the girl" driving, the guys were sure one of them would win. I knew better.

I had learned to drive when my father became ill on the way back from a family trip to Toronto. I drove our 1961 dented grey Chevrolet with a standard shift from the Canadian border to our home in Nyack, New York—a distance of 450 miles. My father stuffed pillows under my seat so that I could sit up higher and look older. I was fourteen years old.

At age sixteen, I received my junior permit, and driving the car was an immediate symbol of power and freedom. Begging my father for the car keys became a ritual, a game I played to attain that freedom and independence. During the wars in Europe, my Russian parents lost everything they had—their health, their home, and their culture. My father became ill with a mysterious stomach ailment, and my mother was depressed by life not turning out as she had planned—after all, she had married the Russian Baron to gain prestige and stability in her life. They had little energy to bring up a headstrong independent girl in America. Left to my own devices, I often felt alone, craving love and affection. My life in our cluttered South Nyack apartment became an inversion of guilt and despair and I was desperate to escape.

It was 1964, the height of the civil rights movement, when even in long-integrated Nyack, there was great unrest between blacks and whites. I was a junior in high school, and although I was aware of the race difficulties, I plunged headfirst into the black world. I met and fell for Joe, a black man in his twenties—tall, handsome, always appearing with a lit cigarette hanging out of his mouth and his lean body draped over a hot, fast, greasy, drag-racing machine. He worked at the Mobil service station in South Nyack as a mechanic—he was an expert on drag-racing cars. Every day, I passed the station on the way home from school and he would notice, call me out, and flirt. After several weeks, I yielded to temptation and walked into Joe's world—a world of romance, sex, and fast quarter-mile drag-racing cars.

For two years, Joe and I were an item—an inseparable love affair. Joe loved his little Russian girl and I loved him. And, of course, there was his car. Everything about Joe's white 1963 Chevy enthralled me—the sound of the engine, the power, the speed. I was filling a hole in my heart with brute forces—horsepower, chrome, steel, and sex.

Joe took me to the noisy quarter-mile drag-car races in New York and in New Jersey. I watched men race their GTOs, souped-up Fords, Chevys, Pontiacs, Buicks. Several times we went to the powder-puff races in Flemington, New Jersey, where women raced cars for the quarter of a mile. I pleaded with Joe to let me compete, and one day, he acquiesced. I won race after race against the girls with our hot '63 Chevy Impala. Again, I had pillows under my seat to make me look older—the minimum age was eighteen. I was under that age, but who was checking? Then, I started smoking the GTOs, the Fords, and the Buicks in the men's races—win after win—going through the gears and keeping my foot on the gas pedal. It was all about the timing. I understood it, felt it, loved it. I loved the speed, the danger. I had nothing to lose.

Tonight, the stakes were high. Joe was betting one hundred dollars that I would win the quarter-mile race. Most of the men were betting against me and putting their money on Snips and his metallic-blue V8 engine, four-on-the-floor Ford Galaxy. It was fast, but was it faster?

I slinked into the driver's seat as Joe got out of the car and walked around to the passenger's seat.

"Now you do everything I say, all right?" he said. "Everything I say, and you do it when I say it."

"Yeah, baby, sure. I know what to do."

Money was exchanged, bets were made, pillows were put under my seat, and I drove the Impala to the starting line, the vibration of the engine beating a rhythm with my heart. I heard some of the men who were gathered to watch the race snicker as I drove to the starting line, but I didn't care. I was ready. Joe and I were going to win this race together. I looked over at Snips in his Ford Galaxy, smiled, and gunned the engine.

The white flag went down, and I popped the clutch. The squeal, the smoke of the tires, and then the gears, first, second, third, fourth...it wasn't enough. The Ford nosed ahead of me doing this *ziggin, zaggin* thing to the right and to the left so I couldn't get by... Joe was yelling in my ear, "Stay cool, baby, stay cool...stay on his bumper...wait till I say..." Then the Galaxy went a fraction too far to the right, giving me a tiny space...and I pressed my foot on the accelerator. The engine roared. I had only seconds.

"HIT IT, HIT IT, HIT IT, GO FOR IT!" Joe screamed. There was a blur of blue and chrome as I passed the Galaxy and then the fine dark nighttime Garden State Parkway was out in front of us with lights and stars going by so fast I could hardly breathe. We crossed the finish line at breakneck speed and slowed to a stop. Men were running toward us. I turned off the engine to pause the vibration in my heart. I felt Joe's arms around me; he was kissing, hugging me. I won. In this moment, I was loved—I was loved for being me, for doing something well. *Hold on to this moment.*

Afterwards we went to Chick n' Charlies Bar in Nyack, where Joe and I split the six-hundred-dollar winnings. I put three hundred dollars in my shoes. The guys bought us a bottle of champagne and put me up on the bar, and I danced and danced and danced…

I was seventeen years old.

At five a.m., I arrived home, climbed two stories up the fire escape, and tugged on the large screen that opened into our apartment. It was locked. I was looking down the barrel of my father's shotgun.

"*Это я, Папа.* (It's me,)" I said.

"*Я знаю.* (I know,)" he said.

He unlocked the screen, let me in, and without another question, turned around and walked to his bed in the kitchen. My mother stared at me from the couch, where she sipped her vodka.

Где ты была? (Where were you?)" she asked.

"*Я танцевала*. (I was dancing,)" I replied.

I walked into my bedroom and closed the door. I lit a cigarette and blew the smoke out of the window. I took the money out of my shoes, my mind racing... *I won...didn't I? It was so close, too close. What if I had lost? Would Joe still love me? Would he leave me? Would I have crashed? I have to keep winning. I have to.*

And Papa? I wish you could have seen me cross that finish line. You would have been so proud. You know the power of the win—you raced horses in your youth, didn't you? Mama? I am so sorry to keep disappointing you. You know how it feels to be in love? How I wish I could talk to you and tell you everything...everything. You are so far away...I can't reach you...

I put out my cigarette, closed my eyes, and began to sob in my pillow before I fell into an uneasy sleep.

THE DANCER FLIES,
THEN CAGED

As performed my Mourka for Read650 on 10/11/15
at the Cell in New York City and for TMI (Too
Much Information)
at the Rosendale Theatre in October 2015 as well.

New York City, 1969. At twenty-two, I decided
that I had to leave my parents, the Baron and Baroness
Meyendorff, sitting with their titles and their piles of
paper, as dusty and outdated as they were, stuffed into
their tiny apartment in the Russian expatriate enclave
of Nyack. I wanted to escape to the Big Apple to make
it as a performer. As the years passed, my mother's
increased exhaustion from working in the sewing
factory and her endless responsibility to cook and to
take care of my father were depressing her. She was
drinking more alcohol, and the apartment was filling

up with my mother's crumpled up poems, vodka bottles—empty and full—drugs, and guilt. I had long given up the idea that my parents were to help me. They had few resources to help themselves. I was flunking out of a two-year college and living in our dark and cluttered apartment, which existed in an inversion of guilt and despair. The camphor-scented mustiness and the claustrophobia of the sick rooms were oppressive. I didn't know what to do with my father's never-ending pain and suffering.

Still the end was unexpected. The day came when the tensions simmered and burned, and with one quick gesture, my mother hurled my bowl of soup at me; it flew through the air like a discus and hit its target. It was hot potato soup that she threw at me the day I told her that I was leaving. The guilt I felt for not wanting to stay home to take care of my parents forced me away from the apartment, into the street. I was leaving for New York City, escaping the sickness and the sadness that permeated our tiny living space, to become an actress.

I left with potato soup on my shoes.

It wasn't long before I was out on the street, angry and broke. Then... I saw an ad in *Backstage* newspaper: "*Go-Go Agent Looking for Girls.*" In desperation, I decided to apply. I knew I was breaking my father's admonition "Aristocrats don't dance!" Maybe go-go could be a step up the ladder?

With trepidation, I walk up three flights of stairs of a towering Midtown Manhattan building, and open the door into a dingy, cluttered office space. I step into the room and am surrounded by hundreds of black-and-white photos of dancing girls revealing their beautiful bodies in a multitude of poses and costumes. *Oh, my God, I could never look like that…* I begin to turn back when the dance agent glances up, takes his feet off the desk, and introduces himself: "Phil." It is too late to run. Phil asks me to put on my costume and do some dance moves. My heart sinks. I don't have a costume yet, I tell him. No problem, just strip down to your underwear, he says. In spite of the initial embarrassment of having to dance in underwear that had seen better days, I close my eyes and slink into a blues number I conjure up in my head. After about thirty seconds, Phil thanks me, hires me on the spot, lends me money for an outfit and gives me the address of my first gig. I am in. To hell with all the nine-to-five secretarial jobs.

With my new black go-go outfit—bra, panties, fringe, fishnet stockings with the seam down the back and red high heels—I take the subway to my first job—an illegal after-hours bar on W. Nineteenth—the warehouse district.

I ring the bell and soon hear the machinery of an elevator. A face appears in the porthole. "Yeah?"

"It's Mourka. Mourka, the dancer?"

A guy by the name of Jerry wearing a suit made out of some slippery silver stuff opens the door with a key. A few creaking lurches up the shaft—God knows how many floors—he opens up another door with a key...

The entire space is wrapped in aluminum foil. Every single thing is glittery silver metal and mirrors. From the middle of the ceiling hangs a silver cage. *Oh, shit!* Jerry leads me into a small dressing room and hands me a large round hatbox.

"Take that off and wrap yourself in this."

"Aluminum foil? I can't dance in aluminum foil."

"So? Dance different."

"Listen, I don't just bump and grind. I'm a jazz dancer. I...dance. I can't dance in aluminum foil."

"Hey. This is what you gotta wear. We got a concept here…"

"Get somebody else."

"What do you mean, get somebody else? I got no time for this shit. All right. Wear what you got, put this on over… No? Jesus Christ. Well add one hundred dollars to what we're paying you… Dese fuckin' artist types."

So I'm dancing in this cage wrapped in aluminum foil. The cage is suspended several feet off the ground. It turns when I turn and swings when I move. I slide in my high heels. I have to hold on to the bars to stay vertical. Yards of foil are shivering and crackling around me. The music blares: the large crowd drinks, smokes weed, ogles, jeers.

At six a.m., I take the subway home with 250 dollars hidden in my shoes. Jerry likes the way I dance and asks me back the next night. I will make more money in two days than I made working a full week at my previous job. I feel rich.

When I tell my mother the Baroness that I am dancing in bars, she tells me in Russian, "Wear a mask and nobody will know it is you."

PART TWO:

A YOUNG WOMAN
OUT IN THE WORLD

THE RETURN OF ANDRE

Four years later, I was still dancing and also acting. I had found my new footing in regional theatre, and I was touring with a play when, without warning, the first love of my life reappeared.

The phone rang at the Tally-Ho Dinner Theatre in Atlanta. It was André. After my initial surprise, I invited him to the show that evening. I could hardly concentrate on what I was doing on stage that night in anticipation of seeing my first love again. The show finally ended. I changed into my best available dress and high heels and walked out to meet him in the theatre lobby.

There stood a man who was only thirty but who looked much older. *Was this André?* The man was bald and overweight. *Where was his wavy hair? His dark eyes?* His dark suit jacket hardly covered his belly, the buttons of his white shirt straining to stayed closed. I didn't know this man. My adolescent dreams vanished the moment I saw him.

André treated me to dinner, and we caught up on our lives. He was in Atlanta on a business trip and saw my name in the local newspaper. There aren't too many Mourkas in Atlanta, so he decided to take a chance and call.

As the evening progressed, André plied me with champagne and proceeded to tell me how unhappy he was with his family, his job, his life. It seemed to me that he was hitting bottom—he also became more and more flirtatious as I was getting higher and higher on the bubbles. After dinner, he invited me to his hotel room for a nightcap. My head was spinning. *Why go up to his hotel room? Surely I can guess what will happen? But what if he doesn't go further? Will I insult him with an assumption?*

We drove to his hotel and rode the elevator to his room. André poured more champagne. He walked away for a moment, and in that silent moment, I stood looking at the filled glass, mustering all my courage to say no.

When André returned, I gathered my purse and jacket and asked him please to take me back to the theatre, where I lived in accommodations above the stage and the restaurant. André became angry and shoved me down on the bed. I pleaded with him to leave me alone. I pushed him off, stood up, and again insisted that he take me home. André pulled himself together and we left the hotel.

We did not speak. I could feel his fury. *How dare I refuse him?* I was afraid of him, but I knew that I had done the right thing. I was so relieved when we pulled up into the theatre parking lot. I turned to him to say good night. Then he took my hand, grabbed my thumb, and wrenched it back as if to break it. I screamed in pain. He let go.

"This is for rejecting me this evening. Never forget me," he said.

I looked into André's glaring eyes, and without a word, I turned away, opened the car door, climbed out, and slowly walked away.

Then, as in a series of flashbacks, I remembered all the incidents, which had seemed inconsequential in my childhood—how he turned me upside down on the big rock, how he chased me through the woods until I was exhausted. Now, I was sure André had a sadistic streak. I wondered, too, about Uncle Vladimir and what really transpired between him and Aunt Irina. And why he, too, had tried to force himself on me. What subtext of cruelty had underscored all our interactions?

I never saw André again. Now, I face an important truth. It had been another time and place, but André's actions, even when he was nineteen and I was twelve, were cruel and I was entitled to be angry. I could have charged him with assault. This is one anger which was belated, but lesson learned. No one, man or woman, would ever get away with hurting me physically, ever again.

MY "ME TOO" MOMENT, CIRCA 1970, OR WHO WAS MY HARVEY WEINSTEIN

It was a half century before the Me Too movement, but human nature, in the form of male lechery upon young female employees, was already thriving. The question was: Could I, would I rebel? And at what personal cost?

My "Harvey Weinstein," Charlie Vreeland, was a bank manager at the Paterson National Bank on Market Street in Paterson, New Jersey. He was a small, bald-headed man of about seventy and had an air of importance about him. He sat enthroned, twiddling his thumbs behind his enormous mahogany desk in the red-carpeted room next to the central area of the bank.

Friday nights the bank stayed open late and the staff worked both the day and evening shifts with time off for dinner. As usual, the busy women tellers were stationed at their windows and the do-little manager men sat in their offices, positioned behind their polished vast mahogany desks.

I was only twenty-three and the new girl on the floor, having worked as a teller for only a few weeks. I didn't particularly like this job, but it was better than my last employment as an operator at Bell Telephone, where, for one glorious day, I worked in the morning, went for lunch, and never returned.

Working with numbers all day was tedious and I didn't like the way the bank staff treated some of the clients. It was 1970, before computers and the internet; client information was written on cards for bank personnel use only. I was appalled to see the word *colored* next to several names.

One morning, early in my employment at the bank, I pulled the alarm next to my knees. I was bored. Within minutes, several very good-looking policemen arrived to stop the robbery and soon discovered my "mistake." I was reprimanded for my clumsiness and made to promise that I would never touch the alarm again. I never did but inwardly I was pleased that I gave this inequitable system a little shake.

On Friday nights, it was always busy at the bank with clients bustling around, filling out forms, standing in lines, and making transactions with the tellers. Charlie Vreeland was always sloshed on Fridays after drinking several martinis during his dinner break. The night in question was no exception—his face was redder than usual, and his incessant drunken giggle permeated the already close atmosphere.

On previous Friday nights, I watched Charlie walk over to the teller department and, one by one, pinch the busy women's asses from behind. None of the women said a word for fear of losing their jobs, or perhaps there were some women who enjoyed the attention, I don't know, but it infuriated me. I dreaded Friday nights. *How would I react if he did this to me?*

For the first few weeks, Charlie had bypassed me—perhaps because I was new. I prepared myself for the onslaught. I had one foot out the door already. It wouldn't take much for me to quit.

On Friday night, the night it came to a head, so to speak, it was particularly busy because of the upcoming Easter holidays. I was speaking to a client and did not see Charlie approach. I was unprepared as I felt his hand squeeze my ass, felt his hot alcohol breath blow on my neck, and heard his piercing laugh in my ears. I screamed as I half fell off the stool, papers and pencils flying through the air. I regained my balance and turned around to see his face turning from a red to a purplish color and I yelled for the entire bank to hear, "Charlie, get your hands off me you…you…you dirty old man!"

Outraged, Charlie fired me on the spot, yelling, "Get out…get out! Never come back!"

I grabbed my purse, picked up my hat and coat, and ran out to the street. I didn't stop running until I reached the corner traffic light, where I mingled with the crowd. I stopped and breathed a sigh of relief in the cool evening air. *I was free.* I glanced back and saw a small crowd gathered at the entrance of the bank— perhaps they thought I robbed it.

On the following Monday morning, I drove to the main offices of the Paterson National Bank. I marched into the executive office and told the director what had transpired on Friday night. I demanded my paycheck and an excellent job recommendation in case I ever wanted to work as a teller in another bank (not likely). I told the director that if I did not receive my paycheck and a written recommendation by the end of the week, I would go to the local newspaper and spill the news about Charlie Vreeland's drinking habits and his pinching practices.

Within days, I received my paycheck and a glowing recommendation from the Paterson National Bank. That week, I said goodbye to Paterson, New Jersey, and moved back to New York City to my sublet on W. Ninety-ninth St. and West End Avenue. Good riddance to straight jobs with ass-pinching managers. I was going back to hitting the New York City pavements, auditioning for shows, and hoping for that lucky break.

BEFORE AIDS

Yesterday, I went to a gynecologist for a checkup. I had not been to a gynecologist in five years and I decided it was time. I really don't have much for a gynecologist to look at as, ten years ago, I had a hysterectomy, not from an illness but from a prolapse. A prolapse occurs when pelvic floor muscles and ligaments stretch and weaken and no longer provide enough support for the uterus. My son, who was born in May of 1983, pushed out my insides when he decided to enter this world. For many years, I tried to heal my muscles with dance, but in the end, gravity won and everything had to come out including the ovaries. "Less organs for cancer to feed upon," the surgeon had said.

During this new post-organ exam, after the initial feet-in-the-stirrups exam, I was taken by surprise when the gynecologist, a woman, asked me how many partners I'd had during my life. At first, I thought this was a kinky question from a disturbed physician, but she was dead serious. She went on to say that, after all, my sexual life began before the AIDS scare, that young people were able to enjoy sex without fear of contracting AIDS. I looked at the gynecologist and in just as serious a tone replied, "Read my memoir and you will learn how many sexual encounters I had in my life." I got dressed and walked out the door.

On the drive home, I thought about what the gynecologist asked and realized how true it was. In my youth, I did have more freedom. As I drove, my mind wandered.

Nineteen sixty-nine. A steamy summer day in Midtown Manhattan. As I was waiting for the street crossing light to turn green, my pocketbook brushed against a young man who was standing next to me. I glanced over to get a look at him. He was handsome, probably in his late twenties, with a Mediterranean dark complexion, high cheekbones, full lips, and almond-shaped dark eyes. My gaze drifted down from his face to his slightly bared chest where his white button-down shirt was opened to the second button. *The heat,* I thought. I lowered my glance to his dark blue jeans covering his thighs, his nice long legs. My attraction was immediate.

Was it my vulnerability that made him take notice? He looked directly at me and smiled. I read the expression on his face—*I have what you need...*

The light turned green.

Together, we crossed the street. Was I that starved for affection? I had had many boyfriends with whom I had sex—but was I ever really pleased, let alone satisfied? At twenty-two, had I ever had an orgasm? In my sexual encounters, I had always been the giver, never the receiver. I thought that's the way it was, that's what women did to hold on to their men, give and never ask for anything in return—the ultimate self-sacrifice in the basement of low self-esteem.

And yet, I knew there was something more, something exciting in lovemaking that I was missing. There were songs, films. Images of ecstatic lovers, women who looked beside themselves with erotic joy. I knew what orgasm was, of course. I could climax for myself but the wonder of orgasm with someone else was still beyond me. I was beginning to think that there was something physically wrong with my body, that my clitoris was too far away or that when I was lying down with a man, I was doing something wrong. Or perhaps it was my mind that was constricted, too self-conscious to let go?

When we reached the other side of the street, the handsome Mediterranean stranger looked at me and read the expression on my face—*I want what you have to give.* We stopped and with a single glance that somehow promised that he was safe and gentle, he took my hand and innocently, like two lovers who knew each other for a longer time, we walked to my apartment on the Upper West Side.

When the elevator door closed on the noise of the crowds and the streets, we embraced. I felt the heat and the excitement of his body as we touched and kissed. We exchanged no words as I opened the door to my apartment. There was nothing to say and everything to experience, to explore, to learn. I felt no fear, just elation. I wanted to let go with this stranger about whom I had no prior knowledge. I believed in him because I wanted to believe in him. I was ready for magic.

I led him into the bedroom, where the Russian icon stared down from the corner niche. Ignoring the stern look of the gilded face of Jesus Christ, I surrendered to my olive-skinned stranger's tender touch as he undressed me, lay me down on the bed, and began to slowly caress and massage my bones and muscles—the curves, the hollows—nothing was left untouched. I was receiving, trusting, melting into intoxication, and letting go of forbidden guilt-laden treasures—this was my moment. *Take it! Take it!* The moment escalated as my fine, handsome, brown-eyed man led me into the world of sensation upon sensation as my body writhed and flooded with orgasm upon orgasm.

Slowly we separated our sweaty bodies—the graceful, harmonious duet had come to an end. My beautiful Mediterranean man asked for nothing. There was no exchange of names, telephone numbers, money. I watched him as he dressed, and I thanked him for this late-afternoon gift—the gift of no longer having to settle for less. I lay back and basked in the sheets that held the scents of our lovemaking. His full lips touched mine for one last time, and then he turned, opened the door, and disappeared into the hot and humid night.

His gift stayed with me—the enduring joy in knowing sexual pleasure. With my second husband, the best lover of all, I am, at seventy years old, safe and healthy and now every night I enjoy the pleasures of that one-night stand.

PART THREE

THE YOUNG WIFE AND MOTHER

THE DICTAPHONE

When did my fear take over? Was it the deep freeze that paralyzed me when we moved to a godforsaken section of the North Country that flash froze me? I turned from a playful, wild, and spirited young woman to a wife afraid to go out? Who became almost literally paralyzed?

One moment seemed to be the exact start of the terror, the erasure of self that led to all that followed...

We were new to Saranac Lake, and I took a job as a waitress at the Dew Drop Inn. The physical chill began at once.

"I'm cold," I said to the owner. "Can I put a sweater on?"

"No, you cannot," the owner replied. "People will not be able to see your waitress uniform. They won't know who you are."

They won't know who you are. That's absurd. But do I really know who I am? What am I doing here? Where am I?

In that instant, I felt myself blown sideways, as if the owner punched me in my stomach and left me crumpled up in the corner of the restaurant. I was changed. In a flash, the person who was free-spirited, who raced cars, who had lovers, who performed in plays and danced, was gone. Instead, I took on a heavy burden of fear and high anxiety, a condition I knew nothing about. I thought I was dying.

"Relax. It's all in your head," my husband, Jeff, answered when I told him how I felt. But the terror stayed within me.

In the fall of 1975, because there was no work to be found for Jeff in the Adirondack Mountains, we moved south to Ellenville, New York, a small town in the armpit of the Shawangunk Mountains. In May, we moved again. This time we moved into the sizzling frying pan metropolis of New York City. But I did not thaw out. I was still struggling emotionally, afraid to go see a psychologist for fear of being put into a madhouse.

The noise, the crowds, the lights, the traffic of the city overwhelmed me, and it took me three months to walk down three flights of stairs and leave our apartment on East Seventy-eighth and York in Manhattan. The word for this condition is *agoraphobic.*

Every morning, Jeff would leave for his new job, a salesman for T. Anthony, an upscale luggage store on Madison Avenue, and would hold the door open for the likes of John Lennon, Mick Jagger, and a myriad of Arab sheiks who would travel to the United States to buy luggage from T. Anthony's. I was alone. I cooked. I read. But I would not go out. Jeff did all the errands and grocery shopped on the way home from work. *What if I flipped out in the street?*

When I expressed my desperation to my husband, Jeff was of little help. He believed that psychologists and therapists were "quacks" and downplayed my feelings. He felt that the irrational fears I was experiencing were of my own doing and that I had to undo them by myself. My past dancing and theatre performances and dreams were "unnecessary frivolities." My Russian aristocratic parents were "sick old people" Jeff had no use for (he had no use for his parents either); Russians generally were not to be trusted and my Russian background was superfluous. I listened to him, afraid to move.

There is a Russian saying, возьми себя в руки, translated loosely as *get your ass into gear*, and three months after we moved into the Big Apple, I tried to do just that. With my heart in my mouth, I got dressed in my finest outfit, walked down the three flights of stairs onto the street, walked cross-town to Second Avenue, and boarded a downtown bus. I was going to a job interview at Macmillan Publishing on Third Avenue and Fifty-third street. I remember the bus driver with his head out the window, sneezing all the way because, as he announced, he was allergic to someone's perfume. I thought he was going to have an accident. Sweat pouring down my face, I wanted to get off the bus and walk home but I was trapped by a crush of passengers standing and swaying in the aisle.

The job interview at Macmillan Publishing Company was on the thirty-third floor. I asked the black security guard at the front door if he would ride up with me. He looked at me like I was from outer space and said, "I can't be riding no elevators with people I don't know—that ain't my job."

"But I'm scared of elevators," I cried out for everyone to hear. Some people laughed.

"Girl, you better get unscared 'cause you just might get the job," he said.

I didn't think of that. I walked back to the elevators with legs trembling. *I've gotten this far; I cannot turn back.* I pressed the up button, my heart pounding. When I got off at the thirty-third floor, I felt the perspiration even behind my knees.

"Are you here for the Dictaphone-typist job?" asked a well-dressed young woman walking in my direction. I nodded.

"Come this way."

I was trapped. I had seen the job listing in the want ads, but *what the hell was a Dictaphone?* I looked around the room and I saw women with earphones on their heads, typing away, and surmised that they were listening to a dictation through, yes, a Dictaphone.

"Have you ever used a Dictaphone?" the young lady continued as we walked.

"Oh, yes," I answered. *How hard could it be?* Soon the woman sat me down in a tiny cubicle next to a few other young ladies in their respective cubicles who were "Dictaphoning." She gave me the little machine that looked like a tape recorder with earphones and told me that she would be back in a few minutes to check on my typing. I was being clocked.

"*Psssst*. How do you work this thing?" I asked the girl next to me after one futile attempt to get it going. She got up from her chair and showed me the works.

"Tell the woman there is something wrong with this Dictaphone and she'll get you another one. This way you won't lose your time."

"I think there is something wrong with this Dictaphone. I couldn't hear very well," I said to the woman who was monitoring me. Without hesitation, she went and got another machine, buying me some time to hone my skills on the first machine. By the time I sat down to type my test, I was proficient. I smiled at my little friend; she smiled back.

I got the job.

For the three months that I worked for Macmillan, this surfacing survival skill held my life in a delicate balance. I was still frightened of the elevator and the bus, exhausted from the effort of overcoming irrational fears. I was afraid of taking medication of any sort and that fear saved me from a lifelong dependency on antidepressants. The mere fact that I was going out every day, concentrating on the mundane typing work that I was doing gave me time to regain my equilibrium enough to live day by day, hour by hour, sometimes minute by minute. As I listened to the Dictaphone and tapped out words, I would repeat the old mantra, "I'm doing the right thing. I'm doing the right thing; I'm doing the right thing…" I began to function again, to feel…

SHINE

Co-written with Sigrid Heath and performed by Mourka for PAW, Woodstock in 1994, at Cuneen Hackett Cultural Institute in 1995, at Theatre 3 in NYC in 1997 and at the Forty-sixth Street Theatre in NYC in 1998. *Shine* was produced by Too Much Information
and performed again by Mourka in February of 2010 at the Rosendale Theatre.

It's 1975 and…I've met this guy. He's my age, blond, blue eyes. He is a writer and very smart. I like that. He sends flowers to m? backstage—I'm wardrobe mistress for the nude Broadway show *Oh! Calcutta!* Light work. He says he loves me. He loves me. I move in with him. Then a letter arrives at our new apartment in Rockland Lake, New York. It's from my father, the

83

Russian baron. *И что вы собираетсе делать?*
(And what are your intentions?)

I marry him. Shortly after our wedding, my young
husband begins a pilgrimage. He brings me along to
cook and to clean and to perform various sexual acts
and to believe in him. I do. I do all those things. I'm
THE WIFE.

His pilgrimage takes us farther and farther north.
When we get to Saranac Lake in the Adirondack
Mountains in late autumn, we stop, right on the edge
of the water. When winter comes and the lake freezes,
we'll continue right across it, walking. Him, slightly
ahead, me slightly behind, one foot in front of the
other. I repeat my mantra: "I'm doing the right thing,
I'm doing the right thing, I'm doing the right thing."

"You must lighten your load, Mourka," my
husband says.

"*Yes, lighten my load... Get rid of my books?
Tolstoy, Chekhov?... Every single chotchke?... Aretha
Franklin, Ray Charles?... The fringed bras and the
fishnet stockings?... Gone. MY LEOTARDS. MY
TIGHTS. My soft red leather jazz shoes...gone.
Nothing left...but rectitude.*"

"Oh, Mama! I'm doing everything I'm supposed to do and it's killing me. Can I stop now?"

"Он хороший человек, Мурка, хороший муж. (He's a nice man, Mourka, a good husband.)"

The Good Husband lies on top of me groaning while I look out over the lake over the blue ice, toward Baffin Bay, toward the frozen top of the world and down the curve of the planet…and I'm interrupted by a tiny collision deep in my flesh. It's accompanied by an explosion—tiny, but absolutely unmistakable. The tentacles of his DNA embrace mine in an ancient dance. One of the Good Husband's blond-haired, blue-eyed sperm has driven into my Russian ovum, and the happy egg has planted itself firmly against the wall of my womb—right here! The zygote staring in mute defiance at the IUD.

Nine months later, still winter, I believe, he drops me off at the trailer with my brand-new baby girl, kisses me on the forehead, and turns to go away "to find himself." I see the terror in his eyes. He sees the terror in mine but pretends he doesn't.

I lay my daughter on the bed and look at her.

"You are so beautiful. And, oh, sweetie, look at all the pretty things I've gotten for you. A little nightgown. Cloth diapers. Powders. Ointments. Booties…PINS! Oh, My God!"

I call my best friend, Lee. She's in Minneapolis.

"Lee! Help!"

"Sorry, darling. I wish I could talk. I'm opening tonight, *Two for the Seesaw.*"

I love that play. That should have been my play.

"You'll be fine, Mourka. *Listen.* It's instinctual," she said. "Just listen to your instincts. Gotta run. I'll call you later."

Oh, yes. Of course. It's instinctual. I just have to listen to my instincts. And what do your instincts tell you, Mourka?

I look at the baby.

My instincts tell me to run as fast as I can. Turn around right now and run and run and run and don't stop running until…

"No, no…don't cry, sweetie. Mommy didn't mean it, really. Please don't cry."

There is a distinct odor coming from the bed.

"What's that?"

I sniff around, then zero in on the baby.

"A diaper? Yup! That's it! A DIRTY DIAPER! Oh, honey, no wonder you were crying. It's okay. I can do this…I think. Here we go."

Slowly and with extreme care, I unpin the diaper.

"Yesssssss…good girl. OOOOOOOH! What a nice poopie, sweetie. I'll put this diaper…I'll put it…what the hell did I do with the diaper pail? I'll… *Don't cry!* I'm here. I'm right here. I'll just put this…on the floor. Yes, that's what I'll do. I'll just put it on the goddamn floor!"

As I put on the clean diaper: "Do you look like me? Do you know that I'm your mama? And you know what else? And this is a secret. Don't tell your Daddy! I'm an actress! Yes, I am. An actress.

"*I am an actress.*"

I walk away from the bed and into another world.

"No, I'm a seagull. He didn't believe in the theatre. He laughed at all my dreams… I am a seagull. No, that's not it… Do you remember you shot a seagull? You came along by chance, saw it, and having nothing better to do, destroyed it."

I come back to the baby.

"Chekhov, sweetie. In this trailer Chekhov and I are incognito, in disguise, and in despair."

I'm back to my own world.

"*I miss it.* I miss it. The performing. I miss the charge, the charge. Like fast cars. Like sex. And it doesn't have to be Chekhov, but you stand there in the wings and you shake and you call on the gods and then you go on and it takes all of your energy and all of your imagination and all of your concentration to tell that story, and then, when it goes well, and it comes back to you from out there, from them, in a great circle, it's like being drunk, like being in love, it's like nothing else in the world, and... What was I saying? Oh ,yes... Turgenev: And may the Lord help all homeless wanderers..."

"Mama, Mama. How will I survive this...this love...this responsibility...this loss of...this longing for...and then the guilt? How did you do it? And I was hard, Mama, I know...I understand a little better and...I'm not cut out for it. I'm just not good at it. And you weren't good at it either, were you, Mama? No, you weren't...but I'm beginning to understand...but I...feel like I'm floating in space. I have no floor. I can't breathe..."

"Clean something, Mourka. There are dishes in the sink. If you wash all the dishes really clean, you won't notice the walls, and when the baby wakes up, they'll be *done*, and when he comes home, all the dishes will sparkle, Mourka. They will sparkle and shine, and when your dishes are all clean, you'll be redeemed, you'll have a life—and make no mistake about it, right now, you HAVE NO LIFE! Do it, Mourka! Faster, Mourka! Faster!"

Wild, agitating of hands in the sink.

SPARKLE! SHINE!

Postscript: It took more years than I care to count to find the courage to survive. I divorced my husband, brought up two children, worked, obtained a master's degree, and above all, I followed my heart—performing, singing, and dancing.

PART FOUR:

DIVORCED AND CHALLENGED

THE HAPPENING

As performed by Mourka for Read650 on 3/19/17
at SUNY ULSTER Theatre

"There's a Halloween costume party tonight up in Palenville," Lynn said on the phone. "I think we should go. It's supposed to be a 'happening.' Rumor has it that the all-male band is performing naked."

"But what are we wearing? Do you have a costume? I don't have a costume," I said.

"No worries. I'll meet you at your house in an hour. Find something to put on," she said. "It will be fun."

And the phone clicked.

Leave it to Lynn, my good friend, a modern dancer and choreographer extraordinaire, to dig up this party in Palenville, a tiny village in upstate New York in the middle of nowhere. My children were with my ex-husband, and I had the night off. Why not?

As I stood loading dirty clothes into the washing machine, I glanced up at the wall of my laundry room at the single decoration—a bright red communist flag with the yellow hammer and sickle insignia in the center. A few years back, I had bought this flag in Moscow and displayed it over the washing machine to depict my daily proletariat tasks.

My inner voice whispered: "Wear it!" Could I go wrapped in a communist flag? After all, Gorbachev's perestroika was in full effect in Russia. I dumped the dirty clothes into the washer, took down the flag, ran upstairs, and stripped. I wrapped the flag around me . . . twice. The mini flag dress fit perfectly from just above my breasts to just above my knees, the hammer and sickle making a perfect design in the middle of my body. I pulled up my hair for formal flair, donned red high heels, and pinned several Russian military medals to my chest. If the band was appearing naked, I could be a Russian general wearing the flag. With safety pins holding me and the flag together, I could hardly walk, much less sit or dance for fear of unraveling.

The door opened and I gasped as Lynn walked in, dressed as the ghost of Martha Graham, holding a large lit candelabra in her black-gloved hands. Her face was white with powder, eyes outlined in heavy black, no lipstick. She was wearing a long, tight black dress with a turtleneck collar and her hair was pulled back tight in a bun with chopsticks protruding. Lynn bore an uncanny resemblance to Martha anyway, but in this outfit, she embodied her. Lynn was dressed to the gills; I was half-naked.

Very careful not to disturb the safety pins and chopsticks, we climbed into the car and headed for the party. We were famished because, in the excitement, we had forgotten to eat. The only recourse was to stop at the drive-through Burger King window at the thruway entrance. We managed to eat our Whoppers without too much movement and continued on our way.

The party was packed with people who were on various levels of alcohol and marijuana highs. Everyone was in a tizzy, awaiting the advertised naked musicians. When four nice-looking musicians finally did appear— yes, naked with glow paint on their *members*, the crowd roared in appreciation. From my perspective, they were a partial disappointment as they quickly hid behind their instruments—the guitar and cello players more successfully than the saxophonist. The rest of the evening, Lynn floated through the crowd with the lit candelabra and I fussed with my communist flag minidress as the heavy Soviet medals were threatening to open and expose my breasts.

The next day the *Kingston Freeman* ran an article on the front page—*Nudity and Commies in Palenville* and named names—a few prominent Woodstock citizens who attended. Had I known there was a right-wing reporter at the gathering, I would have let my flag slip to reveal my "left wing" breast and really given him something to write about.

TOPLESS

How do you think I felt the day it happened? I had just finished a weekly house-cleaning job—washing other people's dirty dishes that were piled up to the ceiling, cleaning up Great Dane puppy shit that was smeared all over the bathroom floor, swishing out toilets, heaving dirty laundry into the washing machine, and mopping and vacuuming their sprawling two-story home. I was forced to hold down several jobs since my ex-husband never gave me enough money to help keep our two kids fed and clothed...

My ex-husband gloated in the wings, waiting for me to fail financially and come crawling back to him.

I would show him. I would show everyone. On that sweltering day in 1992, it became a question of exactly what I would show him and everyone else. I was ready for a meltdown.

August 1992. On the way home from the hellish cleaning job, I heard the car radio newscaster announce that the New York Court of Appeals, in a ruling by Judge Vito Titone, found that "there was no justification in discriminating against women by prohibiting them from removing their tops and exposing their bare chests in public as men are routinely permitted to do."

Yay for Judge Vito Titone.

The newscaster continued, "New York can now join Hawaii, Maine, Ohio, and Texas in their laws where they expressly allow women to go topless in any location where men could do so legally."

It's about time.

In my twenties, I had always bared my breasts when vacationing on beaches in southern France and Italy, where being topless was the norm. I loved the freedom from having to bind my breasts in uncomfortable bras and tight bathing suits. I reveled in the feeling of sun and water on my naked body. Being topless felt natural to me. As a young mother, I nursed my two babies in public, never feeling embarrassment. It was the natural thing to do. My breasts signified my womanhood, and I was proud of being a woman.

I pulled into my driveway in Stone Ridge, paid off the babysitter, turned to my two children, and said, "Jessie (fourteen) and Jarett (nine), get your bathing suits on. We're going to the Rosendale pool." The kids were elated and squealing, ran off to get ready.

We arrived at the Rosendale pool around three p.m. and even though the pool was crowded, I was able to secure one of the sought-after white beach chairs. The kids dove into the water while I spread my blue and white towel on the chair and lay down. I adjusted the back of the chair to a reading position, opened my book, and took off my bathing suit top.

To hell with all cleaning jobs, oppressive ex-husbands, and self-serving men who don't clean their own toilets or wash their own dishes or clean up after their Great Danes.

I heard the siren go off; the loud Rosendale firehouse whistle blows sixteen times at any infraction no matter how large or small—a huge fire or a tiny fender bender. I envisioned the fire volunteers jumping into their cars, turning on their flashing blue lights, and racing toward the firehouse to start the fire engines. I envisioned at least three Rosendale police cars rushing to the scene, the policemen secretly relishing the fact that they now had a purpose. Perhaps even the ambulance would be called in case of an altercation.

The sirens loomed closer. I looked up from my book and saw the police cars and fire engines gathering in the parking lot adjacent to the pool.

Without moving a muscle for fear of being arrested for exposition or lewdness, I beckoned Jarett, my son, who was sitting next to me, to go ask the lifeguard why the police and firemen had rushed to the parking lot. In a few minutes, Jarett returned. "It's because you don't have a bathing suit top on, Mama."

I knew that. Come and arrest me and see what happens. I had visions of winning lawsuits and bank-rolling a bunch of money. *No more cleaning houses. Let them clean their own houses!*

I assured Jarett that I was doing nothing wrong and continued to read while the policemen and a crew of volunteer firemen remained. They stood and stared at my naked breasts through the chain-link fence. It was a standoff. Who would flinch first?

After an hour, I felt a cramp in my side having been in a frozen position for so long. As I tried to turn over in the chair, the book slid out of my hands, and as I attempted to reach for it, the chair flipped over, casting me out on the grass. I stood up, breasts facing the police and the firemen, who looked like toy soldiers standing all together. I slowly wiped the grass off my sweaty body with my blue and white towel, picked up the book, and put my top on. I called Jessie and Jarett to gather their things, and together, we walked to the car.

"Sweet dreams," I said to the motley group standing at the chain-link fence as we passed by.

That evening, I was having a drink with friends at a local bar and overheard a conversation: "Did you hear about the woman who went topless at the Rosendale pool? The police couldn't touch her because of the new law."

I raised my shot of cold vodka: *Thank you, Judge Titone, for a small topless victory.* I drank the vodka down, put on my jacket, and went home.

ADDENDUM

On August 24, 2017, Red Hook resident Jenica Igoe was arrested and charged with two counts of public lewdness for topless gardening in her backyard after an offended passerby snapped a picture of her and brought it to the police. A month later, the charges against Igoe were dropped as it has been legal since 1992 for women to be topless in public in New York State as long as they aren't doing it for the money. Igoe filed suit against the village and the arresting officer, Travis Sterritt, in 2018. On March 5, 2019, US District Court Judge Vincent Bricetti ruled that Igoe could sue Sterritt for false arrest and malicious prosecution, but she could not sue the village for violating her constitutional rights by failing to properly train the officer.

Source: *Daily News* and reprinted in April 2019 issue of *Chronogram*.

FLIPPING THE BIRD

It was near the end of September, the beginning of a new public school year, when Bob Rogers, the principal of Heritage Junior High School, reprimanded me for the third time for coming in late to work. Late to work meant any time after seven ten a.m.—a ghastly hour to start work in any profession. Most teachers lived within a close radius of the school. I lived far north, almost an hour's drive. For me, it was a tight commute—up at five forty-five a.m., meditation, breakfast, get dressed, grab the soup to be warmed up for lunch, and leave the house at six twenty-five for the forty-five-minute drive to the school. Every day for ten years, I made it exactly on time. That is assuming that there was no discrepancy between the school clocks and the world/internet clocks. The beginning of this year, my eleventh at the Heritage Junior High, the school clocks were off about three minutes—just enough time to throw off my perfect schedule. I raced into the school on time, but the clock showed seven thirteen.

Bob Rogers reminded me of a turkey vulture skulking around, looking for prey when he stood by the sign-in sheet every morning. This morning, he snatched the sign-in sheet away from me and screeched,

"Meyendorff, you're late…again. That's it, I'm writing you up."

I mustered up all the courage I could find at that hour of the morning and said,

"If you would correct the school clocks—and you are well aware that there is a discrepancy—there would not be a problem. It's kind of ridiculous."

With that, I turned and continued to my classroom and he stomped off to his office.

Several years after I had started teaching French and English as a second language at Heritage, a series of incompetent principals had brought about a serious student disciplinary problem at our school. The district hired Bob Rogers, a short, overweight, balding man with glasses, as the principal and as the ultimate authority on safety and control. He had a nasal twang in his voice, which escalated when he got angry. I could hear Rogers coming down the hall, screaming at somebody, demonstrating his authority. My body tensed when he came near me or when he spoke to me.

He stalked me. He would call me at home if I took a sick day and would ask me why I was out. "Take some medication and get in here," he would say. He would spy on my classroom. One day, he reprimanded me for having students near my desk while we were playing a language game; he claimed security issues. Sometimes he sent mixed signals. Passing me in the hall, a nasal vulture squawk came from him, "Nice legs, Meyendorff."

One year, my classroom was next to his office and he would complain about the noise. My students were involved in singing rap songs in French, playing language games, and being verbal with their new language skills. When I attempted to explain my teaching techniques, he threatened me with the statement, "Make sure you cross your t's and dot your i's till the end of the year."

For me, Bob was a "good ole boy" who always had an entourage of people around him—Rogers's club, I called it. I saw him bully and intimidate students and other teachers into submission and acceptance of his way of thinking. For him, I was a rebel with a creative streak and the word *nonconformist* written on my brow. I did not want to belong to his club, and he knew it. I was afraid of him, felt uncomfortable around him, and tried my best to avoid him. I was not the only staff member to feel this way. Under Rogers's rule, Heritage did not have a relaxed teaching environment.

And now this. My stomach turned knowing that the story was not over and that before the day ended, there would be an inquisition in his office. Sure enough, a substitute teacher was found to take over my class and I was ordered to meet Roger in his office. It didn't take long for him to summon his whipping boys, the two assistant principals, Dick Boison and Lionel Woodsworth, into his office. The school psychologist was also there and a counselor from the guidance office. The teacher's union representative was not summoned. (Dick Boison was a literal sad sack. Years before, he had a stomach stapling but never bothered to buy new suits to fit his shrunken body. His clothes hung on him, making him look like a scarecrow.) Lionel, a tall African-American, looking very righteous and important, towered over me. (Years later, he was taken out of the school in cuffs for sexually harassing the new female principal).

There they all were, standing in front of the large, clean, polished table in Rogers's office. The door was shut behind me. I was told to sit down, and the interrogation began. Only Bob Roger's spoke. "You don't like how we do things around here? You can be moved, you know. You can even be fired for continuously coming in late. Why don't you move to Newburgh and make it easier on yourself? I'm going to make a serious complaint about you and these fine gentlemen are here as witnesses. Do you have anything to say for yourself?"

I said nothing.

"Get the hell out of here!"

As I stood up, I mumbled something about the clocks being off, but I was too intimidated and frightened to say anything more. I just wanted to get out of there. I hated these men. I walked out of the door into the main office and out into the hall. As I walked, I flashed on an incident in grade school when I was eleven years old. It happened in the '50s, during the Cold War, and I had a sixth-grade teacher who hated Russians. She continually picked on another Russian boy and me, making him cry. I refused to cry and, one day, told her that I hated her. I would not apologize to her nor to the male principal, who repeatedly told me to do so. The teacher took me out of all extracurricular activities, and when students went on a field trip that year, I sat in detention in the second-grade classroom.

Ever since then, I'd maintained a major mistrust of authoritative figures— administrators, bosses of the bully type. I could sense them a mile away and kept my distance. The memory brought a fury into my heart and a rage against Rogers and his cohorts. My good friend Henry, the black security guard who stood in the hall by the front entrance of the school, watched me as I raised my hand high and flipped my middle finger to the direction of the men standing behind Rogers'

closed office door. Henry and I exchanged an understanding look and I continued to my classroom.

I had just arrived at my classroom when I was told that I had to return to Bob Rogers's office. On the way, Henry told me that someone picked up my "bird" on video camera somewhere in the bowels of the school building and sent the video to Rogers.

I entered Rogers's office again, my anger trumping my fear. The men were all still standing where I had left them.

"Did you flip me the middle finger, Meyendorff?" he asked.

"No, I did not."

"Well, I have it here on video. Do you want to see it?" he said.

"No, I don't want to see it. If I wanted to flip you a bird, I would have done it right here in the office and right to your face, Bob. I flipped it in the hallway *to the situation* because I find this entire episode nonsensical and a waste of everybody's time. *Just fix the damn clocks!*"

With that, I turned around and went back to my classroom.

I don't know how I made it through that day. I came home in tears and told my husband everything that occurred, that I probably would get fired. He was shocked at my use of the rude gesture since it was not something that he had ever seen me do. I never used it—until now. I explained that I felt trapped and intimidated and angry and that, at that moment, that's all I could think of doing. He understood that too.

I couldn't sleep. In the morning, I did not change my routine at home, drove the thirty miles, and entered the school on time. I noticed—the clocks were fixed.

During the morning announcements, right after the Pledge of Allegiance, Rogers announced: "The staff can thank Meyendorff for finally syncing the school clocks with the real world." Sometime during that day, Bob Rogers put his arms around me and said,

"We're one big happy family here, aren't we, Meyendorff?"

Bob Rogers's secretary had a small plaster mold made of a middle finger raised up with the words, "For the Situation" engraved underneath. She hid it behind the family photographs she kept on her shelf. For a while, I was the buzz among the teaching staff—they wanted to make tee shirts with the same logo. The incident was never forgotten by the staff or by me.

During my final year of teaching, I gathered enough harassment information on Bob Rogers that, with the union representative present, one day, I marched into his office with a thick folder in my hand. I told Rogers that if he said one more intimidating word to me until the end of the year, I would take him "downtown." This time I raised the manila folder instead of my finger. For the rest of the year, we did not speak to each other, and in June 2011, I retired from public education.

In spite of the harassment, I enjoyed being an educator. For me, teaching was a performance—five times a day, five days a week, twenty-five shows every week. It was a great-paying gig, complete with a pension for the rest of my life. And I would be damned if I would let a dictatorial jerk like Bob Rogers take that away from me.

BONJOUR LA CLASSE

(a one act play)

Cast: A woman in her fifties, a public-school French teacher (Madame Anderson) (age is flexible)

Setting: A classroom in a public junior high school. The Fourth Wall is an imaginary classroom of eighth-grade students. A sliver of the hallway (stage right) is also visible. Window is imagined (stage left). Light switch and telephone are imagined stage right near the door. There is a desk with a chair, slightly offstage center to the left. An extra chair is next to the desk. A blackboard behind the desk.

Madame enters classroom laden with her heavy large briefcase, a boom box, and a lunch container. She is pale, her hair is disheveled, and she looks exhausted. Just inside the door, she puts her load down, straightens up, then with renewed vigor picks up her things again and half carries, half drags her stuff to a large desk just left of center. She wears mismatched shoes.

MADAME

Made it!

Madame sits down and starts rummaging in her pocketbook until she finds her compact mirror and breath drops. She looks at herself in the mirror, shakes her head in disapproval, sticks out her tongue, makes an "ahhh" sound as she puts drops on her tongue. She then takes out her hairbrush and begins combing her hair. She begins to recite the AA Serenity Prayer.

MADAME

God grant me the strength

To accept the things, I cannot change…

Madame sticks out her tongue again and puts more drops on. Rummages for her lipstick, puts it on. She then proceeds to take out her books and notebooks. As she stands up to put the boom box on a chair next to the desk, she notices that she has two different-color shoes on.

MADAME

Merde!

Madame starts laughing hysterically—tears start streaming down her face.

The door opens and a student enters. Madame quickly wipes her tears away.

MADAME

Bonjour, Rebecca! *Comment ça va?*

Me? No, no, nothing is wrong. I'm having a bad moment.

Your father is sick? What's wrong?

He went to the hospital last night? Why?

He had a mild stroke? *Je suis désolée*—that means *I'm sorry*. He'll be all right. Sit down and take it easy… He'll be all right…

Madame turns to the blackboard and starts writing, her back to the classroom, pulling herself together as the students start filing in. She pulls her shoulders down, straightens her jacket, runs her hand through her hair, and turns to the class.

MADAME

(singsong and with great bravado)

Bonjour, *la classe!*

LOUDSPEAKER (OFFSTAGE RECORDED)

I pledge allegiance to the flag…. is heard followed by a moment of silence. Madame has her eyes closed either in rest or in prayer that she makes it through the day.

A loud bell is heard signaling the official beginning of class. Madame shudders at the noise and puts her hand on her head. As she looks down, she notices one of the boys in the front row.

MADAME

Jake, you don't look so good. Are you sick?

What? You're about to throw up? Wait a minute!

Madame runs to the room phone and calls the nurse.

(into the phone) Hi, this is Miss Anderson. Jake Nied is about to throw up. He's coming down.

Hangs up.

To Jake: *Allez, allez, allez,* Go, go. RUN!

Phone rings.

(sweet voice into the phone, holding her head in her hands)

Bonjour… *la classe de Francais.*

To the class: Shhhhhhhhhh, classe, it's the principal calling.

(sweet voice into phone) Hello, Mr. Roberts. You have Shaneisha's mother on the speakerphone and you want me to tell her right now what happened? My class just started… OK. OK!

(to class) *Classe,* shhhhhhhhhhh. I have a parent on the phone.

Oh, bonjour, Madame, I mean, hello, Mrs. Smith. Shaneisha is sitting in In-School-Suspension at the moment for cutting my class. Do you know why she cut my class? Is it because I gave her a zero on the last French quiz for talking during the test? Has she spoken to you about this?

(To the class): Shhhhhhhhhhh.

(Into the phone): No! No! I'm not telling you how to raise your child, Mrs. Smith. No, no, I'm not calling your daughter a cheater, Mrs. Smith…

Well, I see. Well, everyone is entitled to their opinion, Mrs. Smith. Can we talk about this later?

What's that, Mr. Rogers? I should give her the test again? But I... OK. OK. OK...

Puts phone down. Breath...Turns to face the class.

MADAME

Commençons, la classe. Les numeros— d'un a cent, one to a hundred, *s'il vous plaît.*

Madame recites the numbers with the class. As she walks to her desk, she stumbles over the chair, nearly falling on the desk. She straightens up quickly, hoping that nobody noticed. She opens the computer to take attendance.

MADAME

*Un, deux, trois...*Keep going, *s'il vous plaît.* To 100!

Aretez! (Silences the class).

(to a student) Daniel, say *quarante.*

No, it's not *carrot.* Say *quarante! Oui! Mieux.*

(to the class) *Continuez.* Continue counting until the end.

Bien fait...Qui est absent? Shaneisha. *Oui. Je sais.* I know.

Madame finishes attendance, comes to the center of class. Takes a deep breath. Oui, Shantelle?

You need to go the bathroom now? Why didn't you go before class? You had so much time. Is it an emergency?

It is an emergency? *Allez, allez, allez. Depeche toi!* That means *hurry.*

The phone rings. Madame runs to the phone.

(into the phone) OMG! Nick!

Madame turns away from the classroom, opens the door, and steps into the hallway to speak on the phone.

How dare you call me during class…

I don't care about your excuses. I have a class to teach. Leave me alone. I just barely made it to school, waiting for you all night. I can't do this anymore….

(back to the class): Shhhhhhhhhh, *classe.* I can't hear.

Madame (tries to whisper into the phone but her voice becomes loud):

I can't. I just can't. *No, don't call me. Pleaes don't call me. I won't pick up the phone!*

Madame puts the phone down and turns back to the class. She is shaken but holds her composure.

(to class) *Alors. Les jours et les mois, s'il vous plaît. Lundi, mardi*, etc.

A paper airplane whizzes past her and lands at Madame's feet.

(To a student) Pick up *l'avion de papier*, Brandon and put it in the *poubelle.*

(to the class) Yes, *poubelle, poubelle.* It's a funny word for *garbage! Classe*, say *poubelle.* Oui.

Classe, say *l'avion de papier.* Paper airplane. *Très bien.*

Encore classe, les mois: janvier, fevrier, etc.

The door opens and we can assume a teacher is just outside the door. Madame leans out the door as if to answer.

(to person outside her door) Are you kidding me? Last night, the superintendent of schools got caught driving drunk? He fell out of his car? OMG. That's too funny. See you later at lunch duty.

(She closes the door).

(to a student) Oui, Esmeralda?

What? *Mon Dieu!*

Madame looks down at her shoes. The students have noticed the different-color shoes. Madame speaks quickly to cover up her embarrassment.

MADAME

Comment dit-on shoes *en francais? Les Chaussures.* Oui! *Et comment dit-on* brown *en francais?* Oui. *Brune. Et* black? Oui. Oui. *Noir! Bien fait, classe!*

Madame turns to a student. *Calme, calme*, Ellsworth. It's not that funny!

I guess it is that funny. (Madame laughs with the class). Same shoes, different colors. That's how Madame's day started. It's dark at five thirty a.m. when I get dressed. Who can see so early in the morning? Isn't it dark when you get dressed?

(Madame looks out the window).

Oh, my God. I don't believe it. They're carrying Ms. Santoro into an ambulance. What happened?

She fainted? Why?

Someone threw a firecracker down the stairs and it went off as she was coming down? This morning? Already? Why didn't I hear it? It was at seven fifteen a.m.? I was still on the thruway...

OK. Everybody back into their seats.

Eh bien. Continuons. Take out the rap song, *s'il vous plaît.*

Madame starts the rap music on the boom box. This is a French rap by a famous French music group from Paris entitled "Au Royaume Animal." The students are enjoying learning it in French.

MADAME

Avec moi, s'il vous plaît.

The class recites the rap with Madame.

MADAME

Aretez!

Madame stops the music.

Mario, *qu'est-ce que tu fais la bas?* Where are your hands? Put your hands where I can see them. *Merci.* Take out the rap and say it with me…

What do you mean you don't have it? Just share with Carl for today. Why are you always losing things? *Put your hands on the table!*

Madame starts the rap again. A knock on the door.

Madame goes to the door and opens it. Shantelle is finally returning from the bathroom.

Ca va? Shantelle? Everything come out all right? I mean, you feel better?

OK. OK. Just sit down and put your head down for now.

(To the class:) Let's start the rap again.

(Puts music on again. Madame closes her eyes, loses herself in the beat, smiles, starts to move to the rhythm. The class is reciting the rap and she and the class are enjoying the moment…the music is blasting…)

LOUDSPEAKER (off stage)

This is a lockdown.

(Madame turns off music quickly.)

This is a lockdown. A stranger has been seen on the premises.

MADAME

(Madame looks panicked) NICK?

LOUDSPEAKER

Police are coming to check all the classrooms and they are coming with trained dogs. All teachers go into lockdown procedure—lock your doors, shut the windows, pull the blinds, keep the students quiet, and hide them in a corner away from the door. *Lights out!*

(Madame runs around the room turning off lights., shutting windows, pulling down blinds. She is mumbling to herself about Nick possibly being on the premises. (an audible whisper) *I will kill him.*)

Darkness…

MADAME

Merde! Quelle journee! What a day…

No, no, Esmeralda, of course I didn't say a bad word in French. *Mardi, mardi*—Tuesday. Today is Tuesday, isn't it?

OK, it's not Tuesday.

Classe, I'm so sorry this is happening. *Tout le monde*, go sit in that corner. Everybody, *depêchez-vous.* Hurry! *Et silence, s'il vous plaît…* Everybody OK?

Silence!

Everybody falls silent. The phone begins to ring. Madame walks to the phone, puts her hand on the receiver, but does not pick it up. She leans her aching head against the wall. The phone continues to ring.

MADAME

(to the class) Silence!… The dogs… They might sniff us out… *Comment dit-on* dogs *en francais? Oui, les chiens…*

There is a deafening silence for about minute. During this silence Madame closes her eyes…just for a moment.

LOUDSPEAKER

This was a test, only a test. Please resume your classes…

MADAME

OK! *Tout le monde.* Get on your feet and back to your desks and *continuez*! Joey, please turn on the lights. *Merci.*

She walks slowly to the boom box, turns up the volume on the rap (lights and music come on at the same time) as she and the class resume reciting the rap together. The music blares, the lights are bright. Louder. Louder…

END OF PLAY

SERBIA

In July of 1994, my new boyfriend, Nick, invited me to visit his family and friends in Bulgaria. I was happy to accept. I loved to travel, and the trip coincided with my plans to join my friend Lynn Barr and perform with her dance company in Italy.

Nick and I had a great time in Sofia, the capital of Bulgaria, dancing and dining with his friends in all the best restaurants. Later, we spent time in the Bulgarian countryside visiting his mother, who spoiled us and fed us meals prepared from her garden. She lavished us with milk, cheese, and kefir taken from her goats. Unforgettable moments.

It was difficult to leave but when the time came, Nick decided that the most romantic way to go to Italy would be by train. We would travel through picturesque Serbia, stop in the beautiful historic city of

Budapest for a few hours, then pass through the Austrian Alps and the Italian Dolomites before reaching Rimini, an Italian coastal city where I planned to meet up with Lynn.

Nick and I were in the first blush of our affair and our relationship distracted me from the stress of single parenting and trying to make ends meet, which was my reality back in my small town in Upstate New York. I realized later that I must have been existing in a euphoric bubble, and somehow hadn't registered the seriousness of the United States' involvement in the Serbian-Bosnian war. I was not aware of the atrocities and "ethnic cleansing" that was going on in these former Yugoslavian countries. Without reading daily newspapers, I missed the fact that United States Air Force warplanes had shot down four Serbian jets in Bosnia in February, that the United States had bombed a military command in Goražde, Bosnia, in the early part of April and, most ominously, on April fourteenth, the Serbs had taken 150 United Nations personnel as hostages. Later, I learned that Nick was more aware of the political situation but didn't share the information with me. He did not think that the war would affect our travels.

In the last week of July, Nick and I left Sofia on a luxurious fast sleeper train with white lace curtains on the windows. I imagined our train being similar to the famous romantic *Orient Express*, which made trips between Istanbul and Paris in the late 1800s. We inhabited our cozy compartment and sat drinking tea served to us in ornate silver glass holders, smoking cigarettes, and chatting about our travels thus far. I kicked off my red Italian high-heel shoes, stretched out my legs, and rested my feet in Nick's lap. Nick massaged my feet and we giggled as we both relished this moment of bliss and frivolity. We were heading for the Serbian border. Romantic indeed.

When we reached the Bulgarian-Serbian border, two Serbian military men knocked on the glass doors to our compartment and politely asked for our passports. We handed them over. They glanced at the documents and left, taking our passports with them. For fifteen minutes we waited until all the passengers were checked and then the train pulled out of the station. I found it rather odd that the border guards did not immediately return our passports, but I put that thought out of my mind, not wanting anything to undermine my sense of well-being. After all, it was a long trip—they would have plenty of time to return our passports.

In less than an hour, the train stopped at a very small station in the middle of the Serbian countryside. I was just sitting and admiring the fields full of ripe vegetables ready for harvest when I heard a yell, "*Amerikantsi, Amerikantsi.*" Within seconds, the train conductor and two other officials entered our compartment and started grabbing our belongings and yelling something in Serbian. As we rose from our seats, I asked the conductor in Russian what was going on? Nick mumbled something in Bulgarian—Serbs and Bulgarians are Slovaks and use the Cyrillic alphabet like the Russians. We could make ourselves understood. The conductor answered me in broken Russian, "You must leave this train immediately. You are traveling through Serbia without passport. Your passports are at the border. You must wait for the next train back and retrieve your passports."

We were trapped. There was no time to get our things together. The officials grabbed our suitcases and threw them off the train onto the platform. I didn't have enough time to put my heels on. I grabbed them from the floor, and in seconds, Nick and I found ourselves on a train station platform, somewhere in the middle of Serbia. I was in my bare feet, odd bits of clothing were strewn around us, and our two suitcases were lying helter-skelter a few feet away. Our beautiful sleeper train with the curtains in the windows slowly pulled away from the station and out of sight.

"You know, the Serbs are the cruelest people on earth," Nick said to me. "Just read the history books."

"Thank you for that bit of information," I said. "This is hardly the time to tell me this. We are in Serbia now and at these people's mercy. Why didn't we read or watch the news? Why couldn't we have taken a boat around Greece? Now that would have been romantic…"

There was nothing to do but wait…

In an hour, a train pulled into the station and stopped. In Bulgarian and Russian, we explained to the conductor what had happened, that our passports were back at the border and that we had to go back and retrieve them. The conductor was not happy but agreed to let us board as Nick passed him a few US dollars. Passengers stared at us as we squeezed our suitcases through the narrow passage between the seats before finding a place to sit. The old commuter train was packed to the gills with people, packages, and crates filled with chickens. There was a fetid blend of human and animal odor. I held my breath; I didn't care. I just wanted to get our passports and move on.

At the border, which was desolate, in the midst of what looked like dark, unyielding fields, Nick and I were met by a tall Serbian wearing a camouflage military uniform and reeking of alcohol. He was not coherent as we tried to explain in our respective languages that we were just passing through Serbia, that we were not affiliated with any political parties, that we were not spies, that we were innocents on vacation. The drunk Serb did not appear to understand anything we said; we were talking to a wall.

Nick and I were separated, our belongings taken away. Nick was taken God knows where and I was put into a cold room in what appeared to be a military barrack, a shabby structure with several rooms. The drunk Serbian left me and walked into his office across the hall.

I paced. I screamed in every language I could think of—Russian, French, Italian. I did not speak English as I suspected that our "arrest" had something to do with living in America. I was still clueless regarding the extreme political circumstances that surrounded us, but it was clear that our American passports had created this disaster.

I continued to yell to no one in particular—to the walls—that I was an international star, that I was a famous dancer, that I was expected to perform in Italy, that if I didn't arrive in time, people would come looking for me.

All this fell on deaf ears. At one point, I thought I heard a young woman giggling in the Serb's office? *What was going on? Are they making love in there? Are they oblivious to my existence? How dare they? And what was happening with Nick?* I wouldn't allow myself to be afraid. I wouldn't allow myself to think that the Serbs were the cruelest people in the world. I had to stay in survival mode.

Hours later, I glimpsed a woman in the hallway; she was dressed in black with a head scarf covering her face; only her dark eyes showed from a slit in the fabric. She shuffled past my room, looked at me, and put her fingers to her lips hidden behind the scarf—as if to tell me to *be quiet; I will take care of this situation.* She entered the Serb's room. The giggling stopped and a young woman, half-dressed, ran out of the room. I listened as the woman and the drunken Serb exchanged words in Serbian; they argued. In what seemed an eternity, the woman emerged from the Serb's office, nodded to me in passing, and disappeared.

Who was she? Was she his mother? His wife? Was she my guardian angel dressed in black? Who was she?

I kept silent and prayed that, whoever she was, this woman had said something on my behalf. In a few moments, the tall drunken Serb came out of his office and beckoned me into his room. I sat down in front of him; I was trembling, afraid of what he might do. He shuffled papers around on his desk, mumbling something to himself, and put his hand on what I believed to be our passports. *Yes.* He signed something on a piece of paper, inserted it into my passport, and handed me both of the documents. My heart skipped a beat. I took the passports from the drunken Serb without looking up at him, afraid that he would change his mind. The Serb then led me out of the barracks and Nick and I were reunited and taken by jeep to the train station.

There we stood, afraid to say anything, speaking only in whispers and waiting and hoping for the next train north. Nick had been robbed in his room—it could have been worse. We came to the conclusion that the arrest was an exercise in American harassment in retaliation for the bombings. *What stopped the drunken Serb from taking us into the woods and shooting us? We will never know.*

The plan was to board any train that came along that would take us to Nis, one of the bigger cities in

Serbia, and find a train there to take us through to Italy. At last, an old rattling train pulled into the station and we boarded. We sat in ancient uncomfortable seats, our backs leaning against straight wooden boards—a far cry from our previous sleeper train. We stopped at every village to pick up the local peasantry with their chickens and goats. The smell was suffocating. I remember asking myself why my life couldn't be as simple as these peasants', living in the countryside and growing vegetables. My anxiety level rose to an all-time high, imagining what could have been.

Nick and I were at least twelve hours behind schedule to meet Lynn. After several hours of bumping along on this creaking train, we reached Nis, where we scrambled our languages together and found a train that would take us out of Serbia and into Italy. As I had not been robbed at the border, we had just enough money to pay for this train but not much else.

Instead of a nice romantic stop in exotic Budapest, I had twenty stressful minutes to get out of the train, run to the main station, and send a telegram to Lynn to let her know that Nick and I were alive. The Hungarian language, one of the most difficult languages to speak, is not a Slavic language. I hoped that there would be someone in the telegraph office who spoke English. I was also hoping that the American coins that I had left in my pocket would be sufficient to pay for the telegram. I managed everything and had not a moment to lose as I boarded the train and it pulled out of the station.

We passed the Austrian Alps and the Dolomites in Italy in the dark of night and were not able to see them. In the wee hours of the morning, the train pulled into the Rimini station. Hair unwashed and uncombed, suit wrinkled and dusty, I looked like something the cat dragged in, but I didn't care. We took my last coins and hailed a cab to the hotel where Lynn was staying. While Nick took a walk on the beach, I ran into the hotel, up the stairs, opened Lynn's door, and climbed into her bed. Lynn put her arms around me as I sobbed into her pillow. I was safe.

INTERVIEW WITH THE FBI

(as performed by Mourka for Too Much Information
at the Rosendale Theatre, July 2012)

It is September 1997 and I'm out of work. The three-year English-as-a-second-language teaching job in Marlboro, New York, is over because the district is too cheap to pay BOCES to continue the program. For three years, I climbed in and out of my car twelve times a day often in horrendous weather to service five schools in the district—three elementary schools, a junior high, and the high school. I had twenty-five needy students who spoke little or no English and I taught and loved them all.

Good riddance to Marlboro.

But I am out of a job, divorced and a single mom with two children. What now?

I notice an advertisement in one of my Russian educational magazines. It's for the FBI! They're looking for Russian translators to translate various Russian documents into English...*Mmm—various Russian documents, secret documents, classified government documents that I could tell my girlfriends about... This is espionage, James Bond material. I could work at home and sit at my computer and type. I could watch the weather from the window. No more in and out of the car—I'm in.*

I call the FBI and get an appointment.

Two weeks later, Miky, my boyfriend, and I drive up the New York State Thruway to the FBI Building in Albany. The building is ominous, desolate—painted white on the outside with small black-tinted windows. It looks like a giant refrigerator. Miky wants to go home. I am still curious.

Miky does not trust the James Bond attitude that I have assumed all of a sudden. He is Hungarian and in 1956, at the age of twelve, he watched Soviet tanks line up on the outskirts of Budapest at the edge of the cemetery, where his grandmother was buried. The tanks were preparing to roll into the city the next morning—the 1956 Hungarian Revolution was unfolding in front of him. Miky lived in a police state.

He does not want me working for the FBI. He doesn't want the phone tapped. He doesn't want the FBI at the house. He doesn't want the FBI watching the house...but I have made up my mind. I want to stay home, translate on my computer, and get paid for it.

We walk inside the "refrigerator." The building is silent—not a sound except for the *click, click, click* of the heels of the single security guard, who shows me where to take my Russian language test. The FBI needs to know if, in fact, I can read, write, and translate Russian. Of course I can—Russian is my first language. Miky has to stay in the frigid unfriendly entrance and wait for me.

Armed with my Russian/English dictionary, I enter into what looks like a small classroom with large tables, no windows. I am given a long translation from Russian to English and I have an hour to complete the exam. I am alone, concentrating on my task, and I am avoiding the feeling of creepiness that slips in and out of my consciousness as I work. The silence is deafening. *Maybe Miky is right.*

In an hour, a clerk takes my translation and, within several minutes, returns to tell me that I have passed the test and that I will be interviewed shortly. I am taken into another office, where at last I meet a man I believe is my first FBI agent. I am ready.

The agent is a pudgy bald short man wearing thick glasses and a grey suit that looks two sizes too small on him, the buttons of his shirt straining to stay closed. He looks me up and down before telling me in his high, nasal voice to sit down in a chair in front of his cluttered desk. *So much for James Bond.*

Without any introduction, the agent says, "During this interview, you will be hooked up to a lie detector. You must answer each question truthfully or the machine will beep if you give a false answer."

"Fine. I have nothing to hide," I answer, a tremble in my voice.

The agent leads me into another room, and then I see it.

"*Oh, shit! It looks like an electric chair!*"

"This is the lie detector chair," the agent says, as his assistant sits me down into this contraption and proceeds to wrap little black wires around my arms and tape them down with adhesive. My arms are now stuck to the armrests. I cannot move; my heart starts racing.

"There's nothing to be afraid of, is there?" the agent asks. His stare makes me feel otherwise.

"No, not a thing." I stare back, mustering courage.

The agent sits down in front of me, turns on a tape recorder, and the interview begins:

"Names? Give me all the names that you might have signed on a legal document."

"Margarita Meyendorff...Mourka Meyendorff...Mourka Anderson...Mourka."

"Anything else?

"Baronessa Margarita Georgiovna von Meyendorff—my father was a Russian aristocrat."

"Address, the last five addresses?"

"I've moved a lot. New York, Minnesota—did a lot of theatre road shows in the South.

"Travel?"

"Russia."

"Russia? Why?"

"My family is from Russia. I worked as a tour guide."

"Relatives there?"

"A few. I have a cousin who got stuck behind the Iron Curtain. I met him in a subway station in Moscow—he was afraid of meeting a relative from the West. Another time Intourist, the Russian tourist agency, was not happy with me for taking a group of American teachers to a children's camp outside of the St. Petersburg visa radius..." *Why am I being so informative? Why do I feel I have to impress this guy? Do I think the lie detector is reading my thoughts?*

"Very good," the agent said with a slight smile. "Married?"

"Once."

"Children?"

"Two."

"Boyfriends?"

Now he is really getting personal. I can't stand him. Mr.Pudgy, I name him—a long shot from Mr. Bond.

"I had an American husband, then Polish, Russian, Bulgarian boyfriends, and my current friend is Hungarian."

"Languages?"

"Besides Russian and English, French—received my teaching certificate in France."

"Where were you born?"

"Displaced persons camp in Germany."

"Work?"

"Actress, public school teacher."

"Ever work in a bar?"

"I was a go-go dancer."

"A go-go girl?"

"A go-go *dancer!*"

"When? Where?"

"New York City, New Jersey, Upstate New York. In the '60s."

"How long did you do this?"

"About a year… or two."

"Prostitution?"

"NO!!!!!"

"Nude?"

"NO."

"Topless?"

"NO!"

BEEP BEEP BEEP

"OK, OK. I went topless once. I danced. I'm a dancer. I studied dance in New York City. It was a way to earn money for drama schools, dance and voice lessons…. When I was a kid, I wanted to be a spy and a singer…" *Pudgy is not impressed.*

"What is the Hungarian-Russian connection in Rosendale, New York?"

"Hungarian-Russian connection? Oh, my phone message?" I'm living with my Hungarian boyfriend. As a joke, we recorded that message.

These bastards called my house. How dare they?"

"You ever take drugs?

"NO!"

BEEP BEEP BEEP

"What did you take?

"A little marijuana…occasionally."

"Marijuana? That's all?"

"Yes."

BEEP BEEP BEEP

"All right, all right, in my early twenties, I was taking a little speed too. My doctor gave me diet pills when I gained weight from birth control pills. Soon I graduated to black beauties. It was the doctor's fault!"

"When did you smoke the marijuana?"

"I don't know, in 1969? Didn't everybody smoke marijuana in 1969?"

"How much?

"What do you mean how much?"

"How often did you smoke? Once, twice, a week, every day?"

"*I don't know.*"

BEEP BEEP BEEP

I turn to the chair:

"*Shut the fuck up!*"

"*All right, all right*—three to four times a week, but that's it. I stopped a few years later."

Pudgy turns off the tape machine and says, "You are very interesting to us. Born in a displaced persons camp of Russian aristocratic parents, speak Russian, French, and English fluently, traveled in Russia, had problems with the communist way of doing things, live now with a Hungarian but had Polish, Bulgarian, and Russian lovers—basically you went through the whole Eastern Bloc... *but* you smoked marijuana and took drugs."

"That was thirty years ago!"

"It doesn't matter. We can't have drugs in employee history. But because of your unique background, I'm going to call Washington DC right now and see if they will make an exception."

Pudgy leaves and his assistant unplugs me from the lie detector chair.

What a bunch of uptight morons. Am I crazy to think I could work for the FBI? All of these bureaucrats and spies in this building, wherever they are hiding, should be smoking weed. This country would be a lot better off! Miky is right. I'm out of here.

After several minutes, Pudgy returns and announces, "Congratulations. You have passed the FBI interview with flying colors *but* Washington won't hire you because of the marijuana and the drugs that you took."

"Are you kidding? The whole world was flying high on weed in the '60s and you are worried about a little marijuana I smoked thirty years ago?"

I grab my pocketbook and my dictionaries from the table and stomp out of the office. In a moment, I return and face Pudgy.

"And by the way, Goddammit! *I never inhaled!*"

BEEP BEEP BEEP

PART FIVE:

MAKING PEACE

I TOLD YOU
IT'S A SEXY
HOUSE

(a staged monologue)

Teeny, hi. You have a minute to talk? You know I hate the phone, but I have to talk. I'm in trouble. Dr. Ross is selling the house! …

I know. Where are we going to go? The kids and I have been renting here for ten years! It's where I finally got to be independent. You know Jeff waited like a vulture for me to fail, but I didn't. I did it. I went back to school… I got a job. I found this amazing house in the woods with a kind landlady! I could actually afford to live here…and now she has to sell! Where in the world are we going to go? Where am I going to get such a deal?

I did look around. There's nothing for under eight hundred dollars a month. And they're dumps. Compared to this? I can't find anything! I always dreamed of buying a place of my own so I wouldn't be at the mercy of even a nice landlady selling! Where it is *mine*. For keeps!

What? There's a house for sale on Main Street Rosendale? Rosendale—it's a dump! It's Woodstock without the legend, with more rednecks than hippies. It's saloon rural goon city! Sure, Main Street is kind of quaint with the second-story balconies. It looks like the Wild West! And it's wild enough… I can't live on a busy street. I can't live on Main Street in Rosendale. I had a whole mountain behind me. Remember the Rosendale Festival? Remember when I danced solo on the stage by the Rosendale Café? That's all that Rosendale is good for as far as I'm concerned. Get in, get on stage, and get out! Festivals! I mean, it's not a place to live. It's a place to drink. There are six bars.

Yes, we could go to the movies. I admit Rosendale Theatre is a jewel. Mom and Pop Cacchio, the old Italian couple, own it. He runs the projector, and she sells the tickets. Sweet! Remember when old Mrs.

Cacchio gave me a bag of home-grown tomatoes somebody left for her? When the kids were so scared by the movie *The Witches*, they ran out? Mrs. Cacchio felt sorry for me. She was still at the ticket booth and she said, "Yeah, I know, this movie isn't really for kids." It was produced by Jim Henson, who was famous for the Muppets…that's how I made the awful mistake. *But* it was directed by Nicholas Roeg, who was brilliant but creepy. Kids die in his movies! I could have killed myself… My kids ran screaming out of the theatre! And then Mrs. Cacchio gave me the bag of tomatoes *and* all my money back… I love going to the movies there *but* I can't *live* in Rosendale!

All right, all right. Where did you see the ad? *Woodstock Times?* All right, all right, I'll go look at the house. Says "cheap but beautiful"? How cheap? How beautiful? Historic? That means "old dump." I want to live in the woods—have space around me, have a garden. And anyway, I mean, I can't buy anything! I have thirty-two dollars and fifty cents to my name till payday! I just started working in Poughkeepsie. I mean it's great that I can teach Russian but how long is this going to last? Sputnik went up a long time ago!!!… And the kids—they can't live on Main Street. They're used to running around in the woods.

Yeah, that's true, the kids could go to the movies anytime they want… They would love that.

All right, all right. I'll go see the house tomorrow. What do you mean that'll be too late? I better go *now*? That this is "a sexy house?" This house is going to be sold out from under me? I "better hurry?" Okay. Meet me later in front of the Rosendale Theatre—they're playing *The English Patient* tonight…it's a very romantic movie. To be honest, I didn't want to see this movie with a girlfriend—I wanted to see this with a guy—but I have no one to call…

I'm sorry, I'm sorry—I didn't mean it that way. I just mean that if I had a boyfriend, which I don't, I would rather go with him…

No, I enjoy going to the movies with you…OK, I'll see the house first and call you right after…

Teeny! Oh, good. You're there. Mrs. Cacchio is letting me use the phone for a moment. I'm in the box office. I'm so excited. *I bought the house!* I bought it in ten minutes with no money. I can see it from the theatre. We're that close! It's beautiful! It's yellow with pink and melon trim…

No, they are not crazy colors—it's a Victorian. They used to paint three colors like that. It is so cute. It looks like a doll's house. I gave the owner a bum check for three hundred dollars. I don't have three hundred dollars! I told him to hold it for three days, not to touch it, that I would sort it out. I have to have this house. Teeny! I walked in the front door and saw the wide-board floors, three fireplaces, two porches—a Romeo and Juliet porch in the back overlooking the Rondout Creek. All the bedrooms have sinks! It used to be a brothel when the miners worked and lived in Rosendale. Can you imagine all the lovemaking going on upstairs? If only the walls could talk... Yeah! Sexy!... It's got a coal stove...

No, I've never done a coal stove...

What do you mean coal's a lot of work and it's dirty? I know, but coal is cheap... The house has a little garden too—the heck with the woods and the mountain. This garden I can take care of.

Just a minute, Mrs. Cacchio, I'll be off in a second.

Teeny, I have to go.

All right, all right. What kind of chocolate you want? They only have the vending machine. They have Kit Kat. Fifty cents. Would you please hurry down here? We're going to miss the movie.

I know they always run late, but don't be ridiculous late. Teeny, the house was built in 1830—do you believe it? It's got a claw-foot bathtub—that's what finally did it. The sexy claw-foot bathtub!

What do you mean how I'm going to pay for it? I don't know. I just know I have to have this house! I'll ask my brother for five thousand dollars—that's all I will need. The guy who owns it is an artist. He told me all I will need is five thousand dollars down...I have three days...

No, I'm not sure that my brother will come through, but he has to!

What do you mean you don't have the money to get into the movies? It's only two dollars!

OK, OK. I have it! You can pay me back. Bring the ciggies! We'll have a cigarette after the show. Teeny, the house was in *Victorian House* magazine. I can't believe it. I have to have this house. There's a little staircase that goes down to the garden from the Romeo and Juliet porch upstairs.

I'm sorry, Mrs. Cacchio, but I just bought a house across the street and I'm so excited. I'll get off in a second.

Teeny, there are still people coming into the movie. You have time. Just get down here. Oh, my God, there's Nick. I gotta go. He's with someone. Another guy. Someone very handsome. I have to see who it is. Teeny, hurry! Bye!

Wasn't that a great film, Teeny?

Yeah, so romantic. You know the main character was Hungarian. Did you get that? And of course, in the most romantic part of the film, when he's carrying the gorgeous woman he loves out of the cave, some kind of shit falls down on us from the theatre ceiling. *Do you believe it?* I absolutely love the Rosendale Theatre, but I wish they would fix that damn ceiling. Soon they will have to pay us to go to the theatre.

You saw the guy that came with Nick? I just called Nick about him. Works with him. Guess what? He's Hungarian. Just like *The English Patient!* Isn't he handsome? His name is Miklos. Miky for short. No, not Nicky, he's Miky! Pronounced Mickey!… I think he's married…

I want to concentrate on this house I'm buying. Do you believe this is happening to me? I can't wait. Talk to you later. I have to call my brother.

Teeny, I'm so glad you're back. How was Hawaii?

Yeah? *Well, I got the house.* (*SCREAM*). My brother came through. I can't wait for you to see it. I'm in it. I love it, love it, love it. I'm taking baths in the claw-foot tub every night... The best part though? I'm in the house a month. I get a call from guess who? The Hungarian. Miklos, remember? Nick's friend who was at the Rosendale Theatre that night we went. Oh, my God—what a sexy voice on the phone and that accent! Anyway, he asked me to go to the Rosendale Theatre with him...

What wife? She's in Hungary! We went to the theatre and saw *The Red Violin.* He loves music. And guess what, he likes Kit Kat too. (*big giggle*) And in the middle of the movie, the electricity goes out, but do we care? Teeny, I'm crazy about this guy! People started to leave the theatre; they were mad that they couldn't see the film, but we stayed right there...in our seats.

Uh-huh, Uh-huh. Finally, Uncle Tony comes out and spots us and tells us to leave, so we left and went where? Across the street. *To my house!* Isn't that the *bomb*? And guess what, Teeny? Last night he came over here for a drink and well... we made love on the sofa and he left his gold watch. I found it on the sofa this morning. You know what, Teeny? He is it. He's the One! Miklos.

I'm going to marry him! You know what? This *is* a sexy house.

NORTH CAPE MAY

As performed by Mourka for Read650 on 10/23/16
at the Sarah Lawrence College Theatre

I noticed Miky standing at the express counter at the Grand Union in Kingston, New York. He was very handsome. I knew he was Hungarian because we had previously met through my Bulgarian then boyfriend. Miky and I spoke. I couldn't help but notice his low, sexy baritone voice. I told Miky that I would be singing with a Russian ensemble and that I hoped he'd attend the show. He gave me his phone number. Who could know that this little exchange would lead to a "grand union—a blissful marriage of nineteen years?

In 1997 when our romance began, we were broke. I was out of work and launching my one-woman show in NYC and Miky worked three jobs—an engineer for Ulster County, a taxi driver for Kingston Cabs, and a vegetable cutter for a Chinese restaurant. He was putting his daughter and son through Bard College and was in debt up to his ears.

That July, Miky and I decided to go camping in North Cape May, New Jersey—an inexpensive way to enjoy the sandy beaches and warm waters of the Jersey shore. We invested in a spacious tent that could sleep four—we would have none of the tiny claustrophobic tents. We bought a queen-sized air mattress and a pump to make it expand to a luxurious-feeling bed… We brought food, pans, and utensils to cook outdoors, wood for the fire, and several bottles of wine. We packed, hung the bicycles on the bike rack, and set off for the five-hour trip to Cold Spring Campground.

It was hot, well over ninety degrees. We arrived at the campsite early enough to bike to the closest beach. A narrow path through thick woods hanging with wild roses and honeysuckle led us to Higbee Beach on the Delaware Bay. To our surprise, we were greeted by a massive voodoo sign crisscrossed on two timbers and a group of suntanned, smiling naked people, who welcomed us to the nude beach and encouraged us to take off our clothes—which we did. So much for Victorian Cape May and the conservative state of New Jersey. We swam naked in the warm, murky waters of the bay, frolicked on the beach, and watched as the Cape May-Lewes Ferry headed out toward Delaware and disappeared in the mist.

The sun was setting when we got dressed and biked to our campsite. We opened up a bottle of wine as we pitched the tent, inflated the mattress, and started the fire to make dinner. We opened up the second bottle of wine as I scrubbed the potatoes, wrapped them in tin foil, and threw them onto the coals. I made salad and Miky prepared the chicken. He placed the chicken into the frying pan and let it sizzle as we gobbled up the salad. We were famished….and not a little tipsy from the wine.

We heard a kind of a popping squeaky sound coming from the frying pan as bubbles started to form around the pieces of chicken. In our inebriated state, we thought we were hallucinating as the bubbles grew bigger and bigger and the chicken seemed to come to life as it rose as if by magic from the pan. But then we noticed that the chicken had an odd scent, similar to soap…

It *was* soap. I had mistaken the dish soap for olive oil when I started to fry the chicken. Without hesitation, Miky lifted the chicken out of the frying pan, placed it into a sieve, then washed it under the faucet; we then finished frying it in olive oil. A bit fragrant but otherwise delicious! Throughout the dinner, we laughed, and laughed as we stumbled into our bed.

The next morning, we were still laughing as we passed gas that was pungent with perfumed detergent. It didn't matter. We felt effervescent in every sense. We were in love—everything was possible.

Postscript: In the beginning of January 2007, Miky sat naked in the steam room at Williams Lake along with two local town judges who were friends. The conversation turned to marriage and the judges convinced Miky that after ten years of living together, it was time for him to marry me. Soon after, on a moonlit night in our backyard, with glasses of red wine in hand, Miky and I exchanged our personal vows and set the date for the wedding.

A week before the wedding, Miky went to the county clerk and asked for a marriage permit and a dump permit at the same time. He didn't want to make two trips…

On January 28, 2007, on a balmy, uncharacteristically warm day, on the dock at Williams

Lake, we married. The two local judges presided and a handful of good friends were witnesses. A good time was had by all, and for us, a new adventure began as husband and wife.

Of course, we also had our marital spats, not serious, they ranged from competitive to comic. The push-pull that keeps good marriages lively.

WALK DON'T RUN

When I was twelve years old, I had a small poster hanging in my room in Nyack, New York, where I grew up. It was of a young girl talking to her horse before a race and the words underneath were, "I would give everything I have to be the lucky dog today." As a Russian immigrant child, I had this same yearning for love, acceptance, and approval. For years, I struggled and fought my way through life. Failure was not an option. Life was exhausting.

Almost a half century later, I brought this same tempestuous determination to the game of tennis. I was fifty years old when my husband, Miky, started teaching me to play tennis on the clay courts of the Williams Lake Resort in Rosendale, New York. Being the competitive sort, I wanted to play games right away. Winning was awesome; losing was a disaster. I would have meltdowns. I would cry, curse, throw the racket, stomp off the court, and vow that I would never play tennis again. The next day, it was a reversal: "Let's go." I would pick up my tennis bag and we would head off for the courts. Miky had the patience of a saint.

I began watching the professional tennis tournaments on TV. Tennis players, like gladiators, face no one but their opponents, sometime for hours. Even boxers have their trainers and masseurs close by, but a professional tennis player may have no one but a coach sitting in the stands. I was intrigued and challenged by the physical and mental stamina it took to play the game. I noticed that, often, it was the Russian players who screamed and threw their rackets when things were not going their way. *Ahhh*, that Russian soul! That Russian emotional high-strung personality—*do or die, all or nothing*, so little in between. I understood it. I felt it.

My own Russian competitive spirit spurred me on. Sails billowing, I hit the tennis courts, laughing, crying, yelling, fighting. There was no time for loss. I had to win, despite the fact that when I watched the Open and other high-level matches, it was the steely, cold, unemotional, steady players who stayed consistently in the top ten. Those are the players who know how to keep their emotions in check and not let them get in the way of the present moment. I had much to learn. Once, I saw an ad in the Omega Institute brochure in Rhinebeck, New York for a workshop called "The Zen of Tennis." I laughed.

Meltdown after meltdown, spending a fortune on lessons, on new rackets, (having broken a few), buying strings and shoes, I began to notice improvements in my game. I gained strength, accuracy, and a knowledge of the more subtle aspects of tennis—the chess of tennis, in which strategy and psychology entered into playing each stroke. I started to win games, sets, and matches. Miky was no longer allowing me to win and our games became more competitive. One season, I even joined USTA, found my ranking, and competed in a local tournament. I won the championship in my division. I was playing well, but I was not yet relaxed or confident.

It was during a tennis match when the "Walk Don't Run" street sign blazed neon in my mind. I stopped. I looked at a tennis ball in the corner of the court and walked at a deliberate, slow pace to pick it up. Conscious of my slower pace, I reached the service line to serve the ball. I relaxed my shoulders, took a deep breath, and as if for the first time, I tossed the ball up, my serving arm drawing back behind me in the familiar circular motion of the serve. The tennis ball spun in the air and dropped down as the racket made contact in perfect rhythm. In seconds, I arrived at that moment when energy is effortless, and the mind is at rest. I was floating, dancing tennis, feeling joy.

Relearning to live and love is humbling and yet it can be as simple as hitting the tennis ball in the racket's sweet spot and watching it sail for a winner. What I learn on the tennis court, I try to apply to the pickup game of life.

And so I play tennis.

CAR WASH

When my husband, Miky, made the turn onto busy Ulster Avenue in Kingston, I asked him why on earth, of all nights, we had to take this way home, with its gaudy road sprawl of strobe, lit fast-food joints, strip malls, and car dealerships, instead of our usual route, the dark calm of rural Route 209 and Lucas Avenue? Why tonight of all nights, when I was still encapsulated in the bubble of Haydn's 1799 production of *The Creation*, which we had just seen at the Fisher Center at Bard College. We had both been transported by that performance and had floated out on the final "Amen" which never sounded more buoyant or powerful. Every detail had been perfect—the exquisite solos, the billowing silken costumes, the graceful staging. How could we leave that elevated heavenly world, a world without conflict or adversity, for the plain of the mundane?

Miky answered that he wanted to show me the no-touch car wash on Ulster Avenue. This innovation would simplify our car washing and, at this late hour, there would be no lines at the drive-through. Miky's sense of the divine had, apparently, left him back at the concert hall and he was ready for the more practical part of life.

In silence, we drove into the deserted car wash, where the long, horizontal squat brick building offered four openings to enter. They revealed long, ugly water hoses dangling from the ceiling and a panel of buttons on the side wall. But one door yawned open with the exclusive invitation: No-touch wash. Here there were no brushes that looked like cooked green fettuccini noodles that could scratch the gleaming dark blue finish of our new Toyota Prius. This entry posted its higher price of twelve dollars and the open money slot inhaled Miky's offering of a crisp ten-dollar bill and two singles.

We drove our new Prius into this featured section. The doors closed in front and behind us and the sprinkler system began to spray the car with water. The metal squirt bar made one swoop in front of the car to the left, then stopped. All the lights went out except one dim bulb flickering on and off from above. In this anticipatory gloom, we sat and waited. Nothing happened. Perhaps there was a pause before the soap was dispelled? We waited several more long minutes… *Something was wrong*. Miky and I looked at one another in alarm. We were stuck in this car wash, at midnight, with no attendant, or even bystander, in sight.

Miky got out of the car and I shouted for him to get back inside: Watch out for water, electricity—you could get electrocuted! He tugged on a rope that said, *for emergencies only*. He was hanging from it with his feet off the ground, but to no avail. The doors stayed shut in a grim and permanent resistance. He started the engine and rocked the car back and forth, thinking that it might trip some mechanism to begin the soaping process. What next? Asphyxiating gas fumes? I was imagining the headline: "Double Deaths at No Touch Car Wash." Before we succumbed to the carbon monoxide fumes, he turned off the engine, got out of the car, and started pushing on every button he saw, but the doors stayed shut. I sat paralyzed in my seat and envisioned calling 911 and having three police cars, two fire engines, and an ambulance arriving to pry us out of the car wash with the Jaws of Life.

"Haydn was wrong. It's an imperfect world," Miky said as he again stepped out into the dim, flickering light... "There has to be a way out." The nondescript button that he discovered in an obscure corner made a loud buzzing sound, then an electronic shriek. The front door creaked open. We escaped.

The next morning, Miky and I woke up and came to the conclusion that when Josef Haydn's infallible God created water on the second day of *The Creation,* he didn't have the no-touch car wash system in mind.

I called the car wash company to let them know we had almost been entombed. They sent us six car wash coupons as an apology. I have yet to use them.

PART SIX:

PARADISE

A few years ago, Miky and I began to take repeat winter honeymoons, renting a vacation villa in Mexico. There we escaped our frigid Northeastern winters for the worst months and luxuriated in the warmth and beauty of the tropical coast and turquoise seas. As always, paradise came with hidden perils.

THE MORNING WALK

January 2018, dawn, in our bed, in our rented little villa in San Agustinillo on the sea.

As I awoke from a peaceful slumber and opened my eyes, I watched a sliver of the golden sun cast dark blue and purple shadows on the walls—and then I heard a new and terrible sound. A loud rumble came from somewhere deep in the earth; a vibration went through my body as if I touched something hot, electric. I broke out in a sweat; fear gripped my stomach. Seconds later, the bedroom started to tremble. The paintings on the wall slipped and turned sideways. Shutters opened and closed and opened again; dishes in the kitchen rattled; tables and chairs on the balcony flew past our open door. Cleo the cat screeched and ran out of the room. Miky and I held each other, held on to the bed, hoping that we would not fall into a chasm and get swallowed up, praying that the world would stop moving. I heard a moan, a wail from deep inside the earth—then a snap. I held my breath...sudden silence...stillness. I let out my breath and shuddered—a shadow crept into my soul. A shadow and a shiver. The violent shaking might have ceased outside but a quiver remained within me, aftershocks in my soul.

I clung to Miky—I tried to focus. *Will anything be the same again? Will I ever be the same again?* For seven years, I worked hard to get back on my feet after the depression that robbed me of my sense of self. Being born in a displaced person camp for Russian refugees in Germany and, years later, abandoned by my mother, who became lost in the abyss of her own depression, left an aching void in my heart. Years of therapy and soul searching and my talents as an artist helped fill that emotional vacuum but within the five minutes when the earth trembled, I felt my strength leave me, my emotional foundation crumble. *Please, God, don't make me go back to that emptiness, that uncertainty again.*

I had been so joyful, so at peace, these past winter stays in the aptly named blue-and-white La Casa Azul. For six years, every January, my husband, Miky and I had come to the tiny fishing village on the southern

Pacific coast of Mexico and had rented this cozy, immaculate villa set high above the sea.

San Agustinillo was not easy to get to—two days of travel with two flights, lots of wait time, and an hour taxi ride to our little *casita*—but once we got there…it was paradise with only a few tourists who wanted to take the grueling trip.

Inside our *casita* was a large white bedroom with seascape paintings on the walls, a bright, yellow-tiled kitchen, a small bathroom with a solar-heated shower; a large balcony with a blue-tiled floor overlooked the Pacific. A plastic table covered with a flowered tablecloth and plastic chairs enabled us to have our meals on the balcony; a large dark-blue handmade cotton hammock hung in front of the kitchen window. The hammock was perfect for naps and reading in the afternoon. A constant breeze from the sea took away the oppressive heat of the day.

We rented this beautiful home from Yolanda Quintana, an eighty-year-old Mexican woman, who still walked up the hill to yoga every day and often hung upside down from a rope in a yoga inversion position in her own *casita* next door. In the past few years, we found ourselves caring for her, more and more, and every year worried we might not find her there the next winter.

Six years ago, we met Yolanda in San Agustinillo when we were invited to watch a film outdoors, the projector powered by solar energy. Yolanda brought wine; someone brought popcorn. What could be better? We needed a place to stay and Yolanda had the place. To say that luck was on our side was an understatement. We moved in the next day.

Now after the earthquake ended with a final shudder, Cleo the cat reappeared, wondering if her corner of the bed was still there. She jumped up and curled into a ball. I raised my arm, let go of Miky. I could move.

The salt sea air breeze wafted into the room as Miky and I sat on the edge of the bed and listened to the sound of the strong Pacific waves crashing on the shore. As our hearts resumed an almost normal rhythm, we watched the blood-red-orange globe of the sun rise behind the palm tree on our balcony. For ten minutes, the sun sustained the intensity of that color before turning a lighter yellow as it rose above the pale blue sky and the darker blue of the Pacific.

We looked at one another, the question unspoken. *Should we attempt our morning walk?* The morning walk was a ritual. But what would we find outside our *casita* today?

I needed to feel the ground under my feet. Miky nodded. We would venture outside. We climbed out of bed, took our bathing suits off the clothesline behind the kitchen, and put them on—they were still damp from the previous evening. We grabbed our sunglasses and flip-flops and walked down the steps into our garden. We were only a five-minute walk to the white sand beach, but I wondered what we would find? *Is our world here changed?*

At first glance, it seemed not; our *casita* and the grounds still appeared a paradise. The fuchsia bougainvillea caught our attention first as we passed the small, turquoise-colored swimming pool where we swam naked in the moonlight after the water had cooled from the strong daylight sun. Next to the swimming pool was a smaller *casita* with a red-tiled roof and an arbor thick with white, pink, and blue climbing flowers. We walked under this floral canopy and saw the banana trees with their large elephant ear leaves swaying in the breeze.

A little farther down, there were the papaya trees with their pendulous fruit hanging from the crotch of the tree. We pushed aside another row of pink-and-white bougainvillea and found ourselves at the orange metal back door, which led us out of our fantasy garden and into the harsher reality of our Mexican neighbors. Worry gripped me in the gut: *Were they hurt in the earthquake?* After all, last year, in September there was an earthquake with a magnitude of eight point one that killed six people and triggered small *tsunami* waves in the South Pacific near San Agustinillo. Thank goodness, Yolanda was visiting her relatives in Oaxaca.

We descended down the steep cobblestone path, crossed the dirt road toward the beach on the other side. Would we see Tutta, the white short-legged mutt who looked like a dirty mop and always lay in our path? Or was her little body crushed?

Today was no different—at least for Tutta. She was there and so dirty and smelly that even the little dog seemed to sense that she was untouchable—but when she looked up at me with her little black beady eyes, I petted her head and told her that she was beautiful. I was glad that she was alive.

What about the other animals and the people? Have they survived, unhurt?

Are they all alive? The woman who rakes her yard, Eva, our friend, who lives under a house made only of palm leaves? What about that big Mexican family who sleeps in their hammocks? The fishermen? My mind tumbled down the hillside ahead of me, my fears escalating. I had the imagination of disaster, and pictured them buried in rubble.

But there she was—the Mexican lady who raked her red clay yard every morning. Usually she was so preoccupied that she hardly ever paused. Today she looked up and answered our *bon dia* greeting. *Good day*. She was thankful that her yard was not damaged. Across her yard on the left was some broken construction and another yard where two dogs were always chained and who always barked as we pass. They were clearly vicious guard dogs but it wasn't clear what they were guarding—the broken construction, which looked even more broken today, or the near-vacant cement home? The earthquake had shaken the structures; rubble lay on the ground, but the people and the dogs were unharmed.

As we continued our descent to the sea, we saw roosters and hens everywhere—in the palm trees, in the doorways, on the roofs, on the path. The large black roosters with their bright red heads and multicolored feathers strutted their stuff in front of the cackling hens. It was morning—were they discussing the morning's quake? A rooster crowed, perhaps with a more triumphant call than usual.

A little farther on the path, on the right, we came upon the large Mexican family. The grandmother was cooking on an open wood fire; the children were playing, and the adults were eating breakfast or lying in their hammocks. There were at least two or three hammocks per Mexican household, and here all were occupied. I imagined them swaying in the quake, absorbing the shocks better than our bed had.

There was a strong scent of fried tortillas. Cooking and laundry were underway as usual. Water trickled down the path from the washed laundry and the yard was draped with hanging laundry. We sidestepped the rivulets to avoid the dirty, soapy water.

Across the path, the taxi driver, Carlos, lived with his family. His yard was paved over with cement and his two maroon-and-white San Agustinillo Nissan taxis were parked there. On one side of the taxis, there was a shrine filled with votives and pictures of Jesus Christ and the Virgin Mary and on the other side was his hammock. This morning, the white-haired grandmother's prayers seemed more fervent as she sat in front of the shrine and a young girl, Carlos's daughter, swept the yard in silence.

Sweeping was a morning ritual in Mexico. Today, I cherished every gesture. The rhythm of her broom seemed to repeat my thought—*every-thing is normal; everything will be all right. Won't it?*

We exchanged a few rudimentary pleasantries in Spanish with Carlos and continued on our way.

A few steps down, another Mexican household lived with a yellow, green, and red parrot who squawked at us as we passed. Children ran between households or played with their plastic trucks and cars on the path, making them roll down the hill. Wise-looking older women balancing loads on their heads walked with perfect posture up and down the path to deliver their wares. Young men on scooters drove past us with cases filled with chicken and fish, which they sold to the locals. San Agustinillo was waking up and it was business as usual, and it was a mixed assault on the senses, the putrid and the fragrant. The smell of dog shit, urine, wastewater, and pink laundry detergent mingled with the smoke of cooking and garbage fires. We looked up to the bright purple flowered bushes that lined the right side of the path and hoped to inhale a waft of natural, aromatic perfume.

The path flattened out as we neared San Agustinillo's main street. On the corner, on the right, lived a fisherman's family who also owned the corner store where we often bought milk and water on the way back from the beach. The family sat in front of the store having breakfast and here, too, the laundry washing was in full swing—more dirty water to avoid.

Tucked away on the edge of the path was a compost pile where a mother hen had dug a home for her chicks. The day before, we saw a dog playing with the chicks and chasing them helter-skelter. The mother hen would not have any of that nonsense and flew at the dog. The dog sat down on its haunches for a few moments, stunned by the hen's ferocity, then sauntered off. Today, the mother hen had all her little chicks next to her, protected and safe.

On the left was the tiny boarded-up bakery—now closed forever, where last year, every morning, we bought chocolate croissants for our breakfast. We ordered the croissants on the way to the beach and picked them up on our way back. They were still warm from the oven. They cost pennies and were the best croissants we had ever eaten.

The terra-cotta painted Hotel Posada was on the other side of the street and was built thirty years ago by

Laci and Andras who were Hungarian. We crossed the bustling main street, looking both ways for people, cars, trucks, *camionettas* (public transportation pickup trucks) buses, and scooters. Laci and Andras appeared in the doorway. Miky stopped to speak to them in Hungarian, his native language. They told us that on an average every year, Mexico had thirteen hundred earthquakes. This morning's quake was seven on the Richter scale—the epicenter in the Pacific was about one hundred miles out. Nothing to be afraid of.

"Normal," they said. *So everything is okay.* We moved on.

We continued down a small flight of stairs and within twenty feet of the chaos of the dusty main street, we stepped into another world—the beach. We took off our flip-flops and felt the warm white sand between our toes and continued walking toward the sea, where the waves were pounding the shore and then receding, leaving perfect curvy lines in the sand and creating a hard sandy surface upon which to walk. Tiny crabs jumped in and out of their holes, scampering from the water. As we looked at the ever-changing horizon where the Pacific met the sky, a grey mist rose, the horizon broken up by the few rocks jutting out of the sea. Pelicans dove for their breakfast in the breaking waves;

white egrets sat on the rocks waiting for their moment to pounce. A wave washed over our feet.

Today the waves were high, and we saw the red danger flags were up but a few defiant souls on their surfboards were treading water, waiting for the right wave to take them ashore. Red flags were serious. People had drowned here—swept out to sea or plunged to the depths, never to surface. The men who tended the beach ran out every dawn to appraise the different areas and posted the red flags at each designated spot. Each day and each beach would have different conditions. Some were more dangerous than others, while one beach was usually considered safe.

We continued walking along the shore and stopped to speak to some of the people we knew—there were a few Americans and a larger number of Canadians who had discovered this paradise and who, like us, came regularly. The foreigners were upset about the earthquake and Miky told them what we found out about the quake from the Hungarians. "Only a seven on the Richter scale."

I kept silent, still trying to keep the demons at bay. The gospel tune "Nobody Knows the Trouble I've Seen," sung by Louis Armstrong, came to mind...*nobody knows. Was this dawn quake a warning?*

There were local fishermen fishing for sardines and mussels in the sea but today there were more yogis on the beach than usual, saluting the early-morning sun and meditating on the power of the earth. As we neared the place where the fishermen parked their five or six fishing boats on the shore, we smelled the pungent odor of blood and fish. The fishermen had just come ashore from fishing all night and their catch was on the sand, on tarps—bloodied carcasses of shark or dorado, cut up for flash-freezing; the fishermen held sharp massive butcher knives that glistened in the sun.

We knew the drill: from the beach, the fish was loaded into ice trucks and driven to Acapulco, where it was put on a plane and flown to Japan or China. That was where the money was. Some of the fish was driven to local restaurants by taxi and if we didn't forget to take some money with us on our walk, we could buy the fresh fish from the fishermen and take it home to cook. We paid one hundred pesos for one kilo of fish, which translated to five dollars for two pounds of fish. Cheap and delicious—from the sea to the frying pan.

Dogs, swimmers, and people walking on the shore needed to be cautious when a fisherman's boat was attempting to come in from the sea. It was a ritual. One fisherman on the shore lay down five or six logs on the beach, then signaled to the boat waiting in the waves several thousand feet away that the coast was clear for making a landing on shore. The fisherman in the boat then revved up the engine and at full throttle sped the boat onto the beach, turning the engine off as the boat hit the sand. If the boat was not far enough up on the sand, twelve or more fishermen pushed the boat higher. Often bystanders like us helped.

We were still looking for one more person—our friend Ewa who lived in the large open *palapa* (a house covered with palm tree leaves) on the hill facing the ocean. Then we saw the palm roof, and a moment later, Ewa emerged. She waved to us.

Our routine was to visit our three favorite beaches—San Agustinillo, Aragon, and then doubling back, the most placid beach nearest our casita called Rinconcito Playa. We reached the mountain of rocks on the eastern end of San Agustinillo Beach and it was time for us to make a decision—to wade through the strong waves around the jutting sharp rocks to reach Aragon or go around by climbing the steep rocky mountain path? Going through the waves was much shorter but dangerous. The waves were strong and created little pockets or holes near the rocks—our feet could sink into the holes, and once off-balance, we could fall and scrape ourselves on the rocks. Or worse, we could be carried away by a large wave or undertow. A red danger flag fluttered, but on the far end.

Today, my sense of adventure—after all, we were survivors—overcame my vulnerability. We waited for the smallest waves coming in, grabbed each other's hands and waded into the water. The waves crashed against our bodies and receded, giving us just enough time to scramble onto the shore.

We were on Aragon with cliffs on one side and the sea on the other. Here, many more pelicans were swooping down to catch their breakfast or sit on the rocks in groups. Their beaks and pouches made strange-looking patterns on the horizon. On Aragon, there were no other people, and we could take off our bathing suits and be frivolous and free—*demons be damned*. We enjoyed a quick dip and continued on…

We walked to the large rock formation on the far eastern side of Aragon. These rocks marked the end of the majestic Sierra Madre de Sur Mountains where they meet with the Pacific Ocean. We touched them with our fingers to mark our journey and, with that, turned back toward San Agustinillo. It felt good to have the warmth of the sun on our backs. The sun was rising higher in the sky—the day was getting hotter. We re-donned our bathing suits and waded into the strong waves. We were returning to civilization, but our walk was not over—*the best is yet to come.*

At last, we were nearing our final destination—Rinconcito Playa, our favorite swimming beach, which was protected from the waves by large rocks jutting out from the sea. That is, if the red flags were not up signaling danger.

Today, to our surprise, the red flags were not up, and now we could swim far out and not worry about being tossed by waves or being sucked into a riptide. We had the beach to ourselves and I could take off my bathing suit top. We threw our flip-flops and sunglasses onto the beach and we ran our sweaty bodies into the turquoise sea. The water was so clear that we could see our feet and the tiny fishes swimming around them. I saw a wave coming toward me and I dove through it, the water silken on my skin—cool and refreshing.

"*Increible!*" I shouted to Miky in Spanish as I came up for air.

"Rico," Miky answered in Spanish. Indeed, the moment was rich, delicious, exquisite...

Together we swam out to where we could see the end of the rocks, where it was still safe. We dove, we played, we swam—backstroke, crawl, and float, looking up at the endless sky or toward the row of houses, hotels, restaurants, and palm trees that dotted the shore—our little San Agustinillo. We reached what I call "the bobbing area" where we could softly bob up and down in the gentle waves, where our bodies felt light and buoyant from the salt. We could float like this forever. Like children, we could not get enough.

It was difficult to get out of the sea, to shed the weightlessness, the silken cool smoothness of the water, but the sun was rising higher and we wanted to beat the midmorning heat. Breakfast on our balcony beckoned as we walked up on the sand, feeling the weight of the earth. We picked up our sunglasses and flip-flops and headed for home—beautiful Casa Azul on the top of the hill.

An hour and a half had passed since we left our balcony for the morning walk. Our bodies felt strong and supple and a satisfying fatigue set in as we took a cool shower in our garden and sat down at our breakfast table overlooking the sea.

My red danger flags were down, the demons had abated—life could again be lived and breathed. Our morning walk was a healer and a reminder that joy was a rarity in life and lasted for only a moment. I held on to that thought and for now, I was at peace again.

The day had just begun.

CREATURES

I was swimming in a cove, protected from the giant waves of the Mexican surf, when something grazed my arm. I screamed and swam to land as fast as I could. From the shore, I watched as the creature surfaced—it was a small brown and yellow snake that washed up onto the sand. It was dead. This was fortunate because the fishermen who ran to hover over it said that it was a poisonous yellow-bellied sea snake, which usually prefers colder waters and dies in warmer waters, rarely seen alive near the shore. Had it been alive and had bitten me, I would not be sitting here writing this story.

The snake had appeared, a slithering death threat as unexpected as the virus crisis which now hangs over me. Within a few short weeks, the world seems infected with an invisible deadly menace. The news is filled with freakish creature stories—rats have become emboldened in the city, seeking food openly, encouraged to emerge from their hiding places. And of course, the virus itself is tied to a fateful contact with some exotic toxic bat in a far-off Chinese market. I shudder and reprise the series of creepy crawlies I have just left behind on my Mexican vacation, only to return home to frosted Upstate New York, where the native snakes and bugs may not reappear until the weather warms.

Every year my husband, Miky, and I look forward to our five-week vacation in San Agustinillo, a small fishing village on the Pacific coast in southern Mexico. We love Mexico and Casa Azul, our little rented casita in San Agustinillo. In January, the tall palms, citrus, and papaya trees, purple and white bougainvillea, and a technicolor array of other tropical flowers greet us. The eighty-five-degree temperature and the palapa roofs of the Huatulco airport remind us that we have arrived in the tropics—I inhale the fragrant warm air and sigh. Until the creatures begin their sly assault....

In contrast to the exotic vegetation, the animal and the insect world in Mexico can be daunting, even dangerous, particularly for those who, like me, are wimps when it comes to creatures who creep, slide, jump, fly, howl, screech, or God forbid, attack.

It takes a few days to settle into a good night's sleep in our bedroom in the casita, which is wide open to the balcony and the cacophony of night sounds. We hear the ocean waves breaking on the shore and a chorus of cats howling. The raucous symphony starts behind the stone wall, on the steep street adjacent to our home. The feral felines are looking for Cleo, the beautiful red-striped cat, who belongs to the owner but sleeps at my feet every night; pretty and tame, she seems to come with our rental. The howling wakes Cleo and she jumps off the bed and joins the cat crew on our balcony and the rendezvous escalates into an unbearable cat screech. The howling gets me out of bed, and I chase the other cats off the balcony. In a few moments, Cleo returns, glad to fall asleep and curl up between my legs again.

There is also the odd raccoon or skunk that needs to be chased before it eats all our fresh vegetables in the basket that we place on the open windowsill. No sooner than I put my head on my pillow do the roosters wake and sing their song into the morning. The hens screech and cackle in response and I doze between the sounds. But my sleep is interrupted…

I awake to crunching noises. As the dream state fades and reality sinks in, I realize the awful bone crunching is actually happening—right next to our bed. I wake my husband, who can sleep through anything, once even through the four-point-one earthquake that once shook the casita. I shake him and tell him about the crunching. He turns on the light and there is Cleo, our docile innocent little Cleo cat, munching on a small iguana.

"The crunching tiger," Miky calls her as he gets up to fetch the broom. I am horrified to the point of paralysis and cannot move while Miky sweeps up Cleo and the dead iguana, onto the balcony and down the steps. All traces gone. Or so we thought. The next morning, en route to the beach, we pass our little swimming pool, which is located at the bottom of the steps, and there lies the poor iguana, half-eaten, floating in the pool. We quickly get rid of the evidence before someone ventures out to swim in the pool.

There is, of course, an assortment of insects and critters that are always in and around our casita. We love the salamanders that scurry on the walls and make little chirping sounds. Occasionally we see a cockroach or two scurrying over the beautiful Mexican-tiled floor. The cockroaches are large and unspeakably ugly. My eighty-one-year-old landlady steps on them with her shoes. The cockroaches are bigger than her shoes. I can't get near them and always shout for Miky, my hero, to kill them. Cockroaches, the longest living insect in the world, are the only creatures that we destroy without guilt.

While walking on our path to the beach, we take a moment to look down and watch a long line of leaf cutter ants march in single file. From morning until night, they carry pieces of leaves three times bigger than they are. They can devour a citrus tree in one day and they are capable of cutting through human skin. With flip-flops on, I make sure I step over the parade of ants and not on them.

Mosquitos, yes, but I can live with them especially with a dose of citronella before sleep. Every night, Miky wraps himself up in his sheets and looks like a mummy. Inevitably, there is blood on the sheets in the morning, but we never feel a sting and there are never any itchy welts.

Reading at night with one lamp lit and all the windows open, our casita invites a large influx of insects. One evening, I was so engrossed in my book that I did not notice the grasshopper and praying mantis invasion that surrounded me. There were about two dozen large grasshoppers and several praying mantises about three inches in length hanging on the walls. Each and every one was caught and gently put back into the bushes in front of our balcony. Lights out, reading over.

Dogs. I love dogs and there seems to be a great many of them in Mexico in all sizes and colors. Most belong to someone and have collars. Some are leashed, some are not and walk freely. Most dogs are friendly and tag along with us when we walk on the beach. Until this past January, I had never been afraid of dogs, when without warning, I was attacked.

This particular morning, Miky and I had seen two non-descript, short-haired tan-looking dogs on our path to the beach. They were chasing the hens and roosters and anything else that moved. These dogs had no collars and it seemed that they had escaped from somewhere and were being mischievous and unruly and free.

Happy dogs. We didn't pay much attention to them.

One hour later, I found myself walking home alone on the same path. I was almost home when the same two dogs jumped out of a neighbor's yard and leapt, snarling at me. I screamed and yelled and waved my arms, but to no avail. The two dogs were egging each other on, and they were determined to torment me. I was just another moving target for them—a tall chicken with skinny legs and flip-flops for chicken feet. A neighbor heard the screaming and came running out but not before one of the dogs managed to plunge a tooth into my knee and leave a gash with his claws. I was shaken. Never had anything like this happened to me.

Our landlady took a photo of my knee and the image went viral in the San Agustinillo community Facebook to warn others about these dogs. Had it been a smaller person, a child perhaps, this incident might have turned even uglier. A little hydrogen peroxide on the surface of my wound—it was not deep—and not much more was said about the dog bite. Until I returned home to New York.

There, I was told by my doctor that under no uncertain terms, I must get anti-rabies shots immediately, even though two and a half weeks had gone by. I was right on the cusp. If I waited longer and the dog had been rabid, I would die. Rabies is always fatal. There is only a short window to get the antivirus injections. Eight shots in the hospital emergency room to start. Then another four shots spread out over a week and then one shot a week for the next month.

By the next January, I was brave enough to return to San Agustinillo. By now I knew my paradise fairly writhed with creatures, but most were benign.

Sometimes we saw various fish and turtles lying on the beach, dead, having been caught in a fisherman's boat net and washed up on the shore. Crabs run around and duck in and out of their sand holes. Lizards scamper on the rocks. Birds—pelicans, egrets, seagulls, and the vultures who voluntarily clean the beach of all dead creatures—fly and dive for prey. If we are lucky and the time is right, we see baby turtles rush toward the safety of the ocean.

Fishermen, returning from all-night forays far out in the Pacific, butcher their catch with sharp knives right there on the beach, working fast to keep the fish fresh for restaurants or for the freezer trucks that take the fish to Acapulco, and from there, to the Far East. If we are lucky, and the fishermen have enough, we buy a kilo of fish and bring it home for supper. A fish dinner from the ocean straight into the frying pan.

Every year we go on a whaling expedition. We pay Efran, a handsome Mexican man (guapo) three hundred pesos, or about fifteen dollars, to take us out on his twenty-foot tourist boat to search for whales, dolphins, and turtles. We have never been disappointed. Huge whales swim forty feet from our boat and jump in and out of the sea. Schools of dolphin swim next to and under our boat, and large turtles float on top of the waves. Sometimes, the braver souls jump off the boat and swim with the dolphins and the turtles. I'm sorry to say that I am not one of those brave souls.

Last year we visited La Ventanilla, a small village about fifteen minutes from our home in San Agustinillo. The village is an eco-tourism center based on its natural resources—mangroves and lagoons filled with crocodiles, hundreds of exotic birds, turtles, and iguanas. The indigenous Zapotec tribe who live here are dedicated to preserving the ecology of both the sea and the lagoons where these creatures live. It was an extraordinary day trip, gliding through the lagoons in a small boat and watching these creatures live in their environment. I saw a crocodile pounce on its prey, our small boat rocking in the water from his quick movement. I watched as one tourist wanted to take a selfie with a crocodile, the guide whisking him away just in time before the crocodile jowls snapped shut.

One evening, Miky and I went to our neighbor's B and B to watch the Australian Tennis Open final on television. Paulina, the owner, a lovely Irish lady who stayed on in San Agustinillo after her camper broke down back in the 1970s, has the only television in town with a Canadian sports channel. A small crowd of tennis fans gathered in her living room to watch the final match. We were engrossed in the game when there came a blood-curdling scream from the couch area, and three grown people jumped up onto the couch. I followed suit and stood on my chair, knowing that whatever it was the group was screaming about was crawling on the floor. And as I looked down, there it was—a black, ugly scorpion crawling on the floor. There are three colors of scorpion in Mexico: black, brown, and light yellow. The black and brown ones can give you a very painful sting, but are rarely life-threatening unless you are very young, very old, or allergic to the venom. In that case, the bite can kill you. The sting is always painful, burning and numbing.

I dislike killing creatures no matter how ugly they are and would rather see them removed, but this scorpion met its end under the sole of a man's shoe and was then flushed down the toilet. Not a very dignified ending to an imposing, albeit scary-looking creature.

Even though I am a wimp when it comes to creepy-crawly creatures, every year, I challenge myself to feel and experience everything in the Mexican tropics. To be there is to experience life's pleasures along with its dangers. And now I know, existing in the pandemic, that death threats can be everywhere, visible or invisible, creepy crawlies we can see and those who appear only under a microscope. As with every other danger and disease, we can only hope to be spared from the most lethal creatures.

THE FALL

In an instant, everything changed—I lost my footing on the step to the balcony and went flying into a freefall and hit the pristine blue-and-white-tiled floor. What had been a beautiful, peaceful scene looked like carnage—blood, wine, broken glass, and I lay, gasping from pain. The blood oozed along the floor where I lay.

The chilled bottle of rosé that I had been carrying in my hand to fill my glass, to enjoy the last vestiges of a nice wine on a warm summer evening in our casita, had flown up into the air and crashed, sending glass shards in every direction. It took another few seconds to realize I had reached out to break my fall and slashed open my palm on broken glass. Blood mixed with wine seeped onto the bleached-white tennis skirt I was wearing, turning it dark red. I could not move; my ankle, at a strange angle, an impossible angle, was throbbing and sending pain, my mind sending signals that however great I had been feeling a moment ago, this feeling changed to a different and frightening reality.

My husband, Miky, called out for our neighbor, Lori, in the next casita, to help. It took moments for them to find the source of the blood flow—my hand was punctured with glass in three places. As Miky mopped up the blood and wine from the balcony and swept away the shattered glass, Lori tended to the wounds. After what seemed an eternity, I was moved from the balcony floor to my bed and my ankle propped on a pillow and covered with ice. Adrenaline and shock shook my body. I could not move. I could not walk. I didn't comprehend what happened—*a misstep? How?* I imagined I had badly sprained my ankle and cut my hand, but surely our annual Mexican vacation could go on for the three weeks remaining on our planned calendar? The days we loved so much, filled with long walks on the beach, swimming in the sea morning and evening…they would continue, *wouldn't they?*

The next morning, Selena, a good friend and our taxi driver, who was always ready to drive us anywhere we needed to go, stood waiting at our front gate to take us to Puerto Escondido, a tourist town on the Pacific coast that boasts huge surfing waves and had the nearest hospital with X-ray service. It was an hour away from our little casita. How would I manage to descend to the waiting taxi? What had been ordinary walks now appeared threatening, impossible.

There were many steps down from our casita, then a short way past the swimming pool, through the gates, and then to the stone paved road where the taxi was waiting. It was obvious I could not walk. Selena offered to carry me on her back. I gave Selena a hug for that generous offer. I knew that Miky wanted to carry me. *But what if he fell? What if I fell from his back?* I climbed on Miky's back, holding on to his big, strong shoulders. I held my breath while my angel husband carried me all the way to the taxi—once fallen, now frightened and feeling like I would topple at any moment.

On the way to Puerto Escondido in the taxi, it was hot and dusty. The road paralleled the majestic sea most of the way and we passed mountains of watermelon and papaya at the roadside stands. There were groves of mango trees and other exotic fruit, but I could hardly notice. The ankle still throbbed, and my foot pointed at a crazy angle and I began to think: *Can it be broken?* I had never broken a bone before. Surely, it could be adjusted, turned back? The doctors could fix this, couldn't they? *Wasn't it just a twisted ankle?*

Selena stayed with us at the hospital in Puerto Escondido as we received the prognosis from the orthopedic surgeon in Spanish and English—two fractures on both sides of the ankle; there needed to be surgery to insert screws and *what the fuck? A clusterfuck! Say no more!*

The surgeon was prepared to admit me to the hospital right away and have the operation that afternoon, but I balked. I was not prepared for surgery. The recovery time, he said, was three to four months. And how would I have time to recover in a foreign country? We couldn't stay at Casa Azul for that long. On the way back to San Agustinillo, it didn't take long for Miky and me to make the decision to go home and have the surgery in New York. Yes, go home, but the trip itself posed challenges. How would we navigate the airports, get in and out of planes? Every motion seemed to cause more pain, and now I could not forget the fall itself, the risk of another...I obsessed about that fateful moment when I'd crashed. *How could it have happened?* I tried not to give in to a growing unease in me...

When we returned to Casa Azul, I again climbed on Miky's back to reach our little casita on the second floor. But going up the stairs proved to be much more difficult for Miky. We were almost to the top when I felt him stop, and for a moment, I thought we both would fall backwards. In a flash, I saw us both lying on the cement floor, hurt, unable to move. Our friends who gathered around us gasped as they saw Miky strain to reach the top. With one more tremendous effort, he reached the top step, and we were safe. Another disaster averted. From that moment on, I navigated steps one at a time sitting on my butt.

There were distractions. Miky and I had made a lot of friends in our little town of San Agustinillo—Mexican friends as well as friends who, like us, vacationed in Mexico; they came from Canada, United States, Brazil, Poland, Hungary, and other European nations. Every year, in January, we would have our happy reunion on the beach and discuss the events of the past year—who came, who didn't come and why. After my fall, these friends made the pilgrimage, trudged up the hill in the heat, to Casa Azul to see me, to bring wine, food and to console me. I was thankful.

While I lay in my hammock unable to move, looking out toward the sea, I thought of Frida Kahlo, the Mexican artist extraordinaire. If Frida could bear the pain of a broken back and a plaster corset that rendered her motionless for months and if she, despite her restrictions, could still paint, I could bear the pain of my horrific accident and the consequences that were still ahead of me. *Couldn't I?* And this was temporary, wasn't it? Soon, I would resume my daily schedule of tennis, dancing, yoga at home...*wouldn't I?*

One night, I dreamt that my friends in San Agustinillo brought my bed down to the beach and placed it on the sand. I was sitting in the bed wearing a white nightgown and the wind from the Pacific blew warm. I felt the waves lapping up onto the beach and touching the bed.

There were other positive distractions that kept my fears from overwhelming me. I am still in awe at the technology that allowed me to use an outdated tiny Mexican phone from a balcony in a remote village in southwest Mexico to make arrangements with airlines to change travel plans and call doctors in New York to set up necessary appointments.

Wednesday evening, the twenty-second of January, three weeks before our original date of departure, we had a lovely potluck dinner with our friends with whom we share our space in Casa Azul.

The gathering also included Sara and Jerome, who book the reservations for us every year, and of course, Yolanda, our dear friend and owner of Casa Azul, who keeps our home away from home gorgeous and pristine. It is Yolanda who stores our old-fashioned Italian espresso maker in her closet for a year and, every year, in January, greets us with it upon our return.

All the food offerings seemed more wonderful, more cherished than ever before—vegetable salad, ratatouille, fish, fried potatoes, and bottles of wine adorned the several tables that we put together from all of our casitas. Jerome, who was a pastry chef in Paris, baked an apple pastry and Yolanda, an extraordinary artist, spent hours creating the most beautiful and delicious dessert: vanilla ice cream served in tiny terra-cotta flowerpots, lined with bright green bamboo leaves and topped with an exquisite tropical flower.

The next day, Thursday, Selena was once again waiting with her taxi outside the Casa Azul gates. This time she was taking us to the Huatulco airport, where we would begin our long journey home. I had booked wheelchair service from *Huatulco* all the way to New *York, but would it work out? What if the wheelchairs weren't there?* I'd never done this before. And the thought of myself, an athlete, a dancer, a tennis player, in a wheelchair…? Well, I didn't want to dwell on it—this sneak preview into the coming of old age. I was no longer young, but I was fit. *I would recover fast, wouldn't I?*

At Huatulco airport, a tiny airport with *palapa* roofs (palm leaves) covering all the buildings, I wondered how I was going to climb up the stairs to enter the airplane bound for Mexico City. Would all these fellow passengers watch while I slowly climbed the stairs on my butt, my leg stretched out in front of me, one step at a time? But when the time came to board, three very *guapo* (good-looking) Mexican young men strapped me to a chair, lifted me up, and carried me all the way to my seat. "*Muchas gracias,*" I managed to say. They smiled, appreciating my appreciation. For a moment, I forgot about my ankle and the journey ahead of me.

I had dreaded wheelchair service until…I experienced it. The people hired to assist the disabled were expert, eager to assist, and I reasoned it was a good job for them and a necessary assist for me—no bathroom lines, no documents to check, minimal security checks, and no immigration problems.

At JFK airport in New York, however, exiting the plane was problematic. At first, I was able to inch myself toward the airplane exit by leaning on the seats and jumping forward, but when the seats disappeared, I jumped on one leg toward the door and almost fell into a wheelchair held by a lovely Egyptian lady wearing hajib. She rescued me by bringing the wheelchair inside the plane. For this, she was reprimanded by her co-workers. Apparently, the wheelchair assistance people were not allowed to bring the wheelchairs inside the plane. Neither she nor I cared much for the remarks as she whisked Miky and me through immigration, helped retrieve our bags and delivered us straight to my daughter's SUV, waiting for us at the airport handicapped parking.

Handicapped! I didn't want to identify.

The next morning, Friday, at eight thirty a.m., Miky and I were already in the orthopedic surgeon's office in Poughkeepsie, New York, awaiting new X-ray results: two fractures in my left ankle and surgery in four days for insertion of pins and metal—the same prognosis as in Mexico. A six-week recovery period with no weight bearing on the ankle, then an air boot for walking.

"Did this accident happen because I'm over seventy years old?"

The surgeon assured me that my fall could have happened to anyone at any age, that perhaps in the spring, I could resume the dancing and tennis.

It was then that the pit opened in my stomach. I hadn't realized the length of time it would take to recover, and *what if I didn't fully regain my former strength and ability?*

The crash, the true fall happened afterward… later that morning. It was cold as our driver pulled into the driveway of our home in Rosendale. He took our suitcases, backpacks, and guitar out of the car and stacked them near the side door. I crawled onto my fifty-dollar newly bought crutches and stood shivering near our baggage, my ankle wrapped in a makeshift cast and my exposed toes almost touching the snow. Miky ran to unlock the doors and I struggled to enter our cold living room. The driver dragged our baggage in, waited to get paid, and left.

The house was frigid. There was no food, no water, no heat as we turn everything off for the five weeks we go away. It was as if our home, which is usually warm and inviting, was not prepared for our early return. I sat down at our dining room table, put my head down, and cried for the first time since the accident.

Why did I fall? Why? How will I be able to live without walking? I thought of how warm Mexico was and how cold I was in this moment. I thought of our walks on the beach, the warm sand, the bobbing ocean waves, our balcony, my beloved hammock—everything and everybody that we left in San Agustinillo only twenty-four hours ago. I thought of the upcoming surgery and I thought of the endless months of recovery that were still ahead of me and I sobbed into my coat sleeves.

As the warmth of our little propane stove began to relax my body, I thought of Frida again and I thought of my dream, of being in bed on the beach in Mexico and the warm breeze flowing over me. I took off my coat, slid from my chair onto the three steps to the living room. From there, I crawled across the floor and climbed into my armchair. Like a wounded animal, I settled into my familiar place and repeated the mantra that I would say to myself for the next six weeks.

I am home. I am safe.

THE ELEPHANT FALL

Is there a mystical connection between elephants and humans? Would this connection affect me in the most personal ways? By a twist of fate, I was to discover the answer to these questions and respond to the ancient beliefs of the people on the subcontinent who still live amongst the great pachyderms. I would also find a strong bond to one of my dearest friends as we both suffered perilous falls.

In Thailand, the elephants are a symbol of fortune and healing. The superstitious will pay money to pass underneath the beast's body in the hopes of gaining the animal's luck. The saying *An elephant never forgets* derives from the elephant's renowned intelligence and belief that elephants are thoughtful about their actions. They protect their young in maternal circles; they honor their dead in the famous "elephant graveyards." And, according to Thai legend, marriage is like an elephant. The husband is the front legs, choosing the direction, and the wife is the back legs, providing the power.

I own three small hand-carved wooden elephant figurines: the tiny elephants hold their trunks high in the air. (The trunks must be pointed up for good luck.) I inherited them from my mother, who told me years ago that these miniature elephants are symbols of good fortune and that I must keep them forever. I believed her and for forty years have kept them on a special shelf in my study. In 2014, the mystical healing power of my three small elephants was tested.

At five fifteen p.m. on February tenth, 2014, in a nature preserve just north of Chiang Mei in Thailand, a beautiful American woman in her early fifties was thrown from an elephant, free-falling twenty feet into the air and landing on a pile of rocks stacked near the side of the road. On impact, she broke fourteen rib bones and six bones on her spinal column. The woman punctured her kidney and bladder and her lung partially collapsed. As she struggled for breath and went in and out of consciousness from the excruciating pain, the panicked Thai natives picked up her broken body, laid her in a metal trough used for giving water to elephants, and loaded the trough into an old van. One hour later the van transferred her to a location where an ambulance was waiting to bring her to the hospital, yet another hour away. The ambulance had no medical staff or equipment, just the driver and a very young woman who sat holding her hand. The injured woman went into shock—she trembled, and her teeth chattered. She was sure she was going to die. When the ambulance arrived at Chiangmei Ram Hospital, she was barely alive. The emergency doctors injected morphine into her shattered body to induce a coma to immobilize and to stabilize her. Two days later, the surgeons operated because a large blood clot appeared in the lining of the woman's semi-collapsed lung.

The woman's name was Donna Ivy and she was my friend and neighbor in the small Upstate New York town where we lived. When she suffered this terrible accident, I had no idea. I imagined she was off on one of her grand adventures.

Every time I drove through the strange five-corner intersection near her home on Route 32 in Kingston, New York, or crossed the running trail near Route 209 where she biked or ran, I would think of Donna Ivy.

Where is she? What adventure is she on this time? Who is she with? Did she meet Mr. Right? What country is she in? Mexico? Thailand? Bali? China?

Shouldn't she be home already? Why hasn't she called yet?

In the summer of 1992, Donna and I met at an intensive English as a second language (ESL) teaching certification course, which was offered at BOCES, an educational facility in New Paltz. We were already certified public school teachers at that time—I taught Russian in Poughkeepsie and Donna taught special education in New York City. We both wanted to broaden our teaching careers by adding an ESL certification to our repertoire. In 1992, we were striving for independence and financial security, bursting at the seams to make up time for years spent in unhappy marriages and dealing with angry ex-husbands. Although, years before, Donna had taken some jazz dance classes and Russian classes from me when I was trying to make ends meet, it was this eight-week intensive workshop that brought us together and we became close friends.

After successfully completing the course in New Paltz and receiving our certifications, Donna and I decided to sign up for a weekend ESL retreat on Long Island. The retreat provided a room at the Marriott, workshops, food, drinks, the works, all paid for by the New York State educational system.

"Did you know that we are about a half hour from Jones Beach?" I said to Donna. I knew I was lighting the spark of a delicious rebellion.

Donna and I looked around the large media center where hundreds of teachers and administrators were filing in. They held pencils and papers in their hands and were poised for sitting in hard chairs to listen to droning educators lecture for three days. Donna looked back at me and a flash of telepathy passed between us. We knew what they were going to teach. We set down our pencils, rose from our table, walked to the elevator, and rode back up to our room.

Donna grabbed her matching bikini underwear (Donna insisted on always wearing nice matching underwear in case there was an accident and she had to go to the hospital) and I donned a leotard and off we went to spend three lovely days on Jones Beach, sunning and swimming on one of the most pristine ocean beaches on Long Island. We ate seaside lunches of hamburgers and hot dogs with curly French fries, and in the evening, we returned to the Marriott for dinner and to sleep—we considered this a well-deserved vacation.

Donna and I both taught ESL for many years and received consistent evaluations as "excellent." Donna was offered a job at the Onteora School District in Boiceville, New York, and I taught in the Newburgh School District. For the next three decades, our lives often intertwined between full-time teaching, single parenting, my theatrical and singing career, and Donna's passion for travel. Despite our busyness, we had time for a fling or two and we compared notes on the quality of our lovers and what they had to offer...or not.

Donna was a stunning, petite, dark-haired, olive-skinned ball of fire with an infectious laugh. She could work a room, charming everyone with her conversation and wit—she could have been a great politician. In a way, we were physical opposites—I was a blondie, fair-haired and pale, but also petite.

Donna traveled the world whenever she had the opportunity, and I was amazed at her energy and courage. She loved exotic clothing and she dressed in colorful outfits that she carefully chose and bought in the various countries. She said she enjoyed and acknowledged my bohemian life as an actress, dancer, and singer. Somehow, we raised five children between us—Donna had three sons; I had a son and a daughter. But often, we went our separate ways, especially as Donna sought out the most distant destinations.

In 2014, Donna traveled with a friend to Hawaii and Japan and then they both flew to Taiwan to join in the Chinese New Year festivities. The friend had to return to the States and Donna made a decision to travel alone to Thailand and Bali. She had heard of an elephant sanctuary north of the beautiful city of Chiang Mei in Thailand where a group of Thai indigenous natives took care of old, disabled, and abused elephants. Elephants are revered in Thailand. Besides symbols of good fortune, elephants in Thailand are considered to have special healing powers, and at this retreat, the humans were returning the favor to heal the elephants they had rescued. They claimed a strong mystic bond that benefited them all.

Intrigued and curious about the elephant mystique, Donna felt a compulsion to go there. She booked the special visit to the sanctuary for a closer look.

In the early hours of February tenth, on a warm and sunny day, Donna arrived at the elephant sanctuary and joined a group of six tourists preparing to spend a day with the elephants—four handsome men from Brazil and a couple traveling on their honeymoon.

The day was well planned, beginning with a presentation about the sanctuary and the many resident elephants. Then the tourists were allowed to meet the elephants and it was at this time that the natives "chose" an elephant for each tourist, pairing them up according to each individual personality. Donna Ivy, the smallest, the most petite person in the group, was awarded Phujan, the largest elephant, weighing in at nine thousand pounds, because, as the natives explained, "Donna had the biggest personality." Of course Donna had the biggest personality. Even without the Thai language, she charmed the natives, communicating with her sparkling eyes and her gestures and they loved her for it.

Donna also had experience in riding large exotic animals. Six years before, in 2008, at an exclusive resort in the city of Udaipur, just south of Delhi in India, she rode a camel at her eldest son's spectacular wedding. According to Indian tradition, the bride and the bride's family walk and the groom's family is bestowed exotic animals— representatives of the Indian gods. Donna's son Jason, the groom, rode an elephant, Donna and his father, her former husband, rode camels, and her two younger sons, Andy and Eli, rode high-bred white horses. All the animals were bedecked with exquisite handwoven tapestries and fresh flowers.

In the Thai sanctuary, to become more acquainted with their assigned elephants, the tourists were told to put on bathing suits and lead their elephants into a mudhole, where they were to bathe, clean, and brush the elephants, the natives continuing to lecture about elephant special needs and care. Donna enjoyed fussing over Phujan in the mudhole—it made her less afraid of his tremendous size and Phujan enjoyed being spoiled. The friendship had begun.

As the group changed back into their clothing, the natives gave everyone an exquisite handwoven indigenous tunic to put over their clothes. The elephants were used to the smell of the tunics, which further created a familiarity with their riders. Then, it was time to ride the elephants—the moment everyone was anticipating.

The *mahouts* (guides) lifted the tourists onto their elephants and the procession began. The riders rode bareback and barefoot. For three hours, the *mahouts* walked next to each elephant, leading seven riders perched on their magnificent steeds on jungle paths through the back country of northern Thailand. Photos show Donna looking stunning atop her large, regal elephant; she wore colorful batik leggings and the beautiful handwoven Indian top.

Donna was riding one of the largest and most exotic animals in the world and she felt honored. Donna swayed with Phujan's rhythmic walk, her legs straddling both sides of his large belly. To calm herself and the elephant, Donna spoke to Phujan and caressed his magnificent head and shoulders. He flapped his ears in gratitude—they had a language of their own.

Close to five p.m., the procession was nearing the end and the riders and their elephants had to cross a public country lane to return to the reserve. The first four riders crossed the lane safely. Then it was Phujan's turn. As he stepped out into the road, two motorcyclists drove by and revved their engines, which backfired and sent loud explosive noises into the air. Phujan spooked and bolted. Donna screamed "*hoooooww*" the word for *stop* in the indigenous Thai language, but to no avail. Perhaps Donna did not pronounce it correctly and Phujan did not understand? Phujan went into a full gallop and Donna hung on to his neck as long as she could until she flew off Phujan's back twenty feet into the air and fell onto a pile of rubble on the side of the road.

For several days after her surgery, Donna lay in her hospital bed in a morphine delirium, hanging to life by a thread. All three of Donna's sons flew to Thailand to be with their mother and were told that there was only one thing they could do for her: to go to the nature sanctuary, make peace with Phujan and tap into that special elephant healing power… and pray.

When Eli, Donna's youngest son, learned about Donna's fall, he put out an international SOS on the internet so that people would come and visit Donna and aid her in her healing process. Twelve strangers from all parts of the world responded and came to Donna's bedside. News of Donna's fall spread like wildfire and Thai people from every religious sect, including born-again Christians, came to visit and pray. They would hold hands together and make a circle around Donna's hospital bed. The Thai visitors gave her a ring of shredded hair from the tail of an elephant and wound this around her ring finger for healing. Donna's hospital room was filled with flowers and banners and fruit and cards from all over the world.

Donna recovered.

Donna was very thin, down to seventy-nine pounds, but when she was able to sit up in her bed, the

Thai nurses brought Donna beautiful clothing (she had come to Chiang Mei with only a backpack) and dressed her because Donna refused to receive the lines of people who came to visit in a hospital gown. Every day, Donna's hair was brushed and coiffed and fresh flowers were woven into her strands. The nurses gave her manicures and pedicures.

Donna spent two months at Chiangmai Ram Hospital recovering from two surgeries, mending her broken bones, and withdrawing from the morphine. Between physical therapy appointments and her long, painful walks down the long hospital corridors to regain strength, Donna learned to speak enough Thai to better communicate with her handsome doctors and the entourage of nurses who doted on her. Donna was the queen of the Chiangmai Ram Hospital and her reign would not be forgotten.

In 2017, three years after her fall, Donna returned to Thailand, to the Chiangmai Ram Hospital to express her gratitude to the doctors and nurses who saved her life. Lifelong friendships were established.

During this same visit to Thailand, Donna decided to take the trip north to the sanctuary to visit Phujan. It was not an easy decision to return to the place where she nearly lost her life. The accident was still raw in her mind, but she felt that she needed to make peace; she knew that Phujan was part of her healing. She was afraid to see him, to stand next to his enormous body, to hear his breathing, to look into his eyes. She was afraid.

The natives were happy to see her. Immediately, they brought Phujan to her. They had to show him that Donna was alive and well. They fully believed that Phujan was responsible for her recovery.

One of the *mahouts* asked Donna if Phujan could wrap his trunk around her waist. Donna hesitated. She remembered how her ribs were crushed and broken by the fall. She was nervous, yet curious as to what would happen. She agreed. After all, she and this extraordinary creature shared a powerful connection of strong character, bold personality, endurance, determination, and pure will. Their lives were forever linked by this near-fatal disaster.

This huge, magnificent animal wrapped his trunk gently around Donna's waist and held her in his embrace for just a moment. Then Phujan let go of Donna, shook his massive head, raised his trunk, and trumpeted a loud roar of joy. There was no doubt in anybody's mind that Phujan remembered Donna, his petite friend who fell off his back. Phujan remembered and he rejoiced in his own elephant way.

When I learned about her accident and terrible injuries, I knelt in front of my little office shelf with my mother's gift of the three tiny elephants and I prayed for Donna's recovery. Weeks after her accident, when Donna was well enough to speak on the phone, she would call me from Thailand, and we had long discussions about her accident. I was so happy that my friend was alive and well. It was, in fact, a miracle that she was alive. Donna was still in pain, but she was healing and getting stronger. I was fascinated by her story and the circumstances around her unique adventure. Although it was difficult for Donna to speak about her fall, to remember some of the horrific details, little by little, she was able to articulate what had occurred.

Just before her release from Chiangmai Ram Hospital, as she was preparing for her painful sixteen-hour flight home, I asked her one more question that was burning in my mind:

"Just curious, Donna, did you have matching underwear when you fell?"

"Of course!" she answered.

We giggled. Donna has style even when she's flying off an elephant.

I had begun my story about Donna's elephant fall in 2014 but life and work got in the way of completing it.

Then, as fate would have it, I broke my ankle in two places during our winter sojourn in Mexico and had to fly home for surgery. The prognosis was disturbing: I would not be able to walk, much less dance or play tennis or do yoga, for three to four months and I despaired. Without the daily routines that I enjoyed so much, I felt vulnerable and depressed. I sank down, resting my head on the table, and sobbed.

Then one day, I glanced over to the special shelf in my study and spotted my elephant shrine with the three carved wooden elephants with their trunks waving upward. The shrine was just as it was in 2014 when I knelt in front of it and prayed for Donna's recovery. I was gripped with a sadness that these living, majestic, powerful creatures were close to extinction. I knew then that I could sit with my ankle in a hard cast (my injury nothing compared to Donna's) and write, and finish Donna's elephant fall story. It would be my ode to Donna's recovery, to our friendship, and to the healing powers of the elephant, which I now firmly believe.

And what of the special elephant hair ring they gave Donna to wear until they predicted it would gradually disintegrate? Donna kept this on her finger for many years until one day when she felt fully restored to her own exuberant self, the elephant hair ring drifted off and seemed to vanish into thin air.

COVID-19 HAIR:
SILVER LININGS

For the last decade, my friends have made this transition—the synthetic brunettes and redheads stopped dying their hair and let it grow out…grey. Not me. I was not ready. I kept my appointments at a chic hair salon called RAGE and the hairdresser dyed my hair so well with a lovely light auburn/blonde tint, even I forgot what color my real hair was. I told my friends when they suggested that I might be happier "going natural" and stopping the dye jobs: "I'm not ready."

Then in March 2020, with the sudden horror of a sci fi film, New York State shut down. Covid-19 was killing hundreds of people a day. There was, according to the experts, "community transmission." Businesses were shut down. Especially businesses where crowds could gather or close contact might occur. Beauty salons were deemed dangerous. RAGE shut down and my cut-and-color package was no longer available. I would be forced to rely on moisturizers and hair dye from Rite-Aid.

Masked and wearing gloves, I tiptoed to the drugstore and, for the first time, bought the boxed dye, which featured a gorgeous model on the box, tossing her lustrous locks. Was that when my doubt took root? I was seventy-two, in excellent shape from my daily workouts—yoga, African dance, tennis, careful diet. For seventy-two, I was shapely but who would I be kidding with this packet of Ms. Lustrous Locks? I was a half century older than she was.

I took a hard look at the center white stripe that had appeared, defining my new hair growth. Was I ready?

Would I be getting greyer by the day? What was I going to look like on screen during my Zoom yoga classes? Should I put make up on at eight thirty in the morning? When this quarantine was over, would people recognize me? Would I emerge from this pandemic an old woman? My husband was beginning to look like a Hasidic Jew with his long grey curly sideburns, and my eyebrows were disappearing.

My hairdresser at Rage offered to do my hair at her house but I declined. I still had the presence of mind to put my life, my health ahead of my anti-aging obsession. But what to do? Was I ready to go grey?

Every morning, I looked in the mirror and saw the rapid-growing ring of grey hair around my face. I realized when I combed my hair and pulled it back with plastic combs, this was exactly what my mother did with her mousy-grey hair. Day by day, I was looking more like her. The sexy reddish-blonde hair faded fast and I started weaving what's left of the color segments into a braid, which was already shoulder length. How was this happening so quickly?

In my culture, Russian ethnic girls maintained their long hair in a single braid. When I was sixteen, my braid extended below my waist, I braved a visit to a hairdresser and asked her to lop it off. I was finished with the hair-combing struggles and hours of washing and drying hair. I was ready. I'd had enough of the braid hairstyle that made me look like the Russian immigrant that I was. I wanted something modern, hip. At first, the hairdresser didn't want to do it, but I insisted. The instant the braid fell on the floor, my hair splayed out into a hundred directions. I looked like a scarecrow. Little did I know that I had exchanged hours of combing struggles for a new world of large pink spongy curlers, bobby pins, and hairspray.

When I got home and showed my parents the braid, which looked like a long dead chestnut-colored animal, they nearly had heart failure.

And now, almost a half century later, I again have a braid.

I started wearing scarves to hide the grey. With a scarf, I looked like a cross between a *babushka* (Russian for grandmother) and an aging gypsy. I dressed up to take the garbage out. The few times it was necessary for me to enter a store, I felt like a character in a science fiction horror film—grey hair, sunglasses, plastic gloves, and a mask over my nose and mouth.

Our surreal science fiction horror movie world continues to rage. People are dying; people are screaming with rage and injustice; people are freaking out from boredom at home. I realize the only thing I can do to help the insanity of this world pandemic is to stay home, remain healthy, and not become a burden to the already overwhelmed front-line workers. I am self-quarantined at home and left to my own devices—like the queen in the *Snow White* fairy tale, I look into the mirror and watch myself turn from sexy red to unsexy grey.

Now, three months into Covid 19: It is not easy, but I learn to relax. Then I relax some more, and when I think I am totally at ease, I mellow out even more. Panic attacks and calling my shrink are no longer an option. I discover that I love being home, that I cherish the quiet—no more traffic noise on Main Street; no one is screaming on the street; no groups of people are barbecuing, grilling, and eating their meals on the sidewalk, no drunken brawls. Residents of Rosendale, the town where I live, are quiet and following the restrictions in the face of the pandemic.

Of course, I miss seeing my friends and going to restaurants and to the movies across the street at the Rosendale Theatre, but I am, in fact, relishing the noncommittal life I am leading. There are no schedules other than my own—jazz dancing in the living room, Russian gypsy guitar playing to nourish my Russian soul, a daily hour of Spanish in hopes of traveling to Mexico again, and in the evenings, I write short stories. During the week, there are Zoom yoga and more Spanish classes. I am busy—too busy to stare into the mirror and watch the reddish-blonde fade away.

The days rush by, and one day, I notice that the grey in my hair is no longer grey, but white—snow white—soft white, wavy, natural. I can't believe it.

With the combs, I pull back my white hair and braid the rest down my back. I slowly turn to get a good look. I like it. It's graceful, peaceful.

I give away the hair dye box that I bought from Rite-Aid.

June twenty-third, 2020. With phase three of the pandemic, my local hair salons reopen. I don't make an appointment—no more salons for me—no more chemicals in my hair. Is that really me? I still stress about Covid, politics, the upcoming election, the fact that some idiot let out the groundhog I caught in the Have a Heart Trap and it's eating my garden, but I consider this transition in me. I decide that I like the profound change in my appearance, and most of all, I like this acceptance of myself.

Yet another level of peace. I'm keeping it. I am ready.

PART SEVEN:

RESOLUTIONS

I find that life and memory are a round trip, and I return now to my memories and thoughts of my mother.

SOUP

I grew up on soup. In our tiny apartment in Nyack, which resembled an overstocked, neglected antique store stuffed with oversized furniture, Russian *chachkas*, and photographs of dead Russian aristocrats, every day for lunch we had soup. In a kitchen that smelled of oil paint and turpentine because the kitchen doubled as Papa's painting studio and bedroom, Mama would prepare the soup. She was not a very good cook. In fact, she didn't like cooking at all and made soups so that she didn't have to cook every day. She also made soups because my father had a mysterious illness and could not digest food unless it was cooked to death and mushy. Soups were liquid sustenance for him, and his stomach pains were less acute. The doctors didn't know what was wrong with my father and did exploratory surgeries to find out. By the end of his life, they had taken out three-quarters of his stomach. Now I think perhaps it was his deep disappointments in life and inner rage that curdled, turned toxic inside.

Preparing food was stressful for my mother, who would prefer to write poetry and make *tchotchkes* from the myriad of wrapping paper, fabric, and furs and ribbons and threads that she kept in boxes under the beds. Trapped in a world not of her choosing, Mama fought depression and self-medicated herself with vodka and amphetamines.

Born in Russia of Estonian parents, when Mama was twelve years old, she lost her own mother to kidney disease. Her heart broken, Mama, her father, and brother returned to Estonia in 1922, fleeing the looming civil war in southern Russia.

Back in Estonia, the years passed, and at age thirty-five, by then a divorcée with two sons from her first marriage, Mama fell in love and married Baron George Meyendorff, my father, a Russian aristocrat living on his family estate in Estonia. For Mother, this was the answer to her prayers. She and her two children would be taken care of and she could live in relative comfort and safety. WWII changed all that when the Soviets invaded Estonia in 1941 and the Meyendorffs, like many of the Russian aristocrats living in Estonia, were forced to flee through Nazi Germany and into Western

Germany. Mama's dream of tranquility was shattered. The family, including my two half-brothers, finally landed in a Russian displaced person camp in West Germany, where I was born in 1947. Three years later, the family of five immigrated to the United States. Mama, shell-shocked and uprooted from two World Wars, found life difficult in America with the new language, with having to work in sweatshops to make ends meet, and with the realization that her charming baron husband was ill and aging.

Nevertheless, Mama did manage to make a tasty Russian Borscht (my favorite), using canned beets instead of fresh beets, to quicken the process. Another one of my favorite soups was sorrel soup, formally known as *schav*. Mama made it for Easter because it's eaten with sour cream and hard-boiled eggs. She used frozen spinach as a substitute for sorrel, which was bit hard to come by, and she didn't realize fresh spinach was actually easier to use. Mama did her best. This soup was delicious anyway.

Several years went by as I struggled to make a living in the theatre. Like my mother, I never liked cooking, especially for myself. There was one very cheap and easy meal that I consistently made for myself. I would boil potatoes (I had to get my quota of potatoes—it's a Russian thing), fry up a couple of hot dogs with onions, and smother everything with canned tomato sauce. Soup making was way too long and tedious.

I inherited some of my mother's fears, anxieties, and depression and married a Prince Charming who would take care of me and make the fears disappear. But Prince Charming came with his own baggage and dirty laundry and the fairy tale evaporated, leaving me alone with two children.

In the 1980s I began teaching public school. I would grab a couple of sandwiches for lunch, drop my children at their respective schools, and continue on to work. It wasn't long before I became exhausted from the workload and became very sick—flu, fever, and a cough that would not quit. Antibiotics were not helping, and my doctor suggested I see an acupuncturist. The acupuncturist took my pulse, poked me with a few needles, and told me that my body was cold and tired. She asked me if I had changed my diet when I started my full-time teaching job. I told her about the daily hot soups that my mother used to make when I was growing up, that now I had little time to stand in front of the stove. The acupuncturist suggested that I bring hot soup to work and eat it for lunch every day.

For the twenty years that I worked in public school education, I brought hot soup for lunch on a daily basis, even during the warmer months, and I never got sick.

I enjoy cooking now. My husband and I have a schedule. He cooks on Thursday, Friday, and Saturday and I cook on Sunday, Monday, and Wednesday and the person who cooks does not do dishes. Tuesday is our play day when we play tennis on a senior men's team (I'm the only woman on the team—I like that). After tennis, a necessary trip to the steam room at the YMCA to ensure that we can still walk for the next couple of days. After the steam, we take turns picking a nice place to have lunch before heading for home. *Life is good.*

On our specified days, we both cook up a large pot of something so that there are leftovers, and we don't stand over the stove as much. My husband, Miky, delves into his Hungarian cuisine, which consists of spicy meat and vegetables dishes. I specialize in soups.

At least one of my scheduled days is dedicated to making soup. It puts me at ease, centers me. Whether it's dropping an organic chicken into a large pot with celery, garlic, and onions to make a broth for a chicken vegetable soup or cutting up the beets, potatoes, carrots, and cabbage for a borscht, I am comforted by the smells permeating every wall in my home and the warmth of the soup simmering in my sunlit kitchen.

If only I could share a bowl of soup with my mama and thank her for the life her soups gave me. If only I could tell her how many salty tears dropped into the soup as I thought of how much Mama gave when there was little to give. If only I could tell her how peaceful I feel when I make soup. *If only I could tell her that I love her.*

RENDEZVOUS

I arrive first, brimming with anticipation—I had waited a long time for this encounter. To calm myself, I order a glass of chilled rosé and a shot of cold Stolichnaya vodka for her and I wait; my mind is filled with our past. Why can't I recall what she called me in my childhood? Mourka? Mourik? Never Mourechka, the most endearing... Did I ever take her to a nice restaurant where she could be pampered and spoiled with delicious food and drink? Never. Tonight, I will lavish and spoil her with a high-end delicious French dinner, the best wine, the best vodka... *Will she be angry? Affectionate? Will we have enough make-up time?*

I notice her when she first appears at the entrance of the café. She is standing and waiting for the maître d' to show her to our table. She has on an unremarkable grey coat and a grey chapeau that covers her grey hair.

She was never very tall; her shoulders droop a little more now and she clutches her pocketbook as she searches the café for a familiar face.

I beckon her to our table. I stand up as she comes toward me. We stare at each other, not knowing exactly what to say, then we embrace. The embrace is awkward as there weren't too many embraces back then.

She takes off her coat and hat and sits down, lights a cigarette, and looks at me as if to say, *Why did you bring me here?* She is as I remember her. She is dressed in a white blouse and black skirt below her knees— simple but still elegant. Her grey thick wavy hair is pulled back with brown plastic combs and her pale oval face is covered with wrinkles. I see that she has made an effort and has applied some mascara and put on red lipstick, but she can never hide that perpetual sadness that permeates her entire being. Even when she was young and beautiful and her skin soft and unmarked, she had that sad, faraway look.

She looks beautiful to me.

The last time I saw her, she was in an alcoholic daze trying to focus on a bridge game with my father, my future husband, and me. In her eyes, I was getting married and doing the right thing for the first time in my life. I knew I was losing my soul. Five years later, I was living in Minneapolis with my husband and two-year-old daughter when my mother fell on the floor with a cigarette in one hand and a shot of vodka in the other. A week later, she died of a massive stroke.

I break the silence.

"Мама," I say in Russian, the language we share, Можем ли мы начать всё сначала?" (*Can we start over?*)

She puts out her cigarette, swallows the shot of vodka, then takes my hands in hers.

"Можем." (*We can.*)

We hold hands and look at each other. This is not an apparition. It is Mama. I saw tears well up in her eyes and start to run down her cheeks.

We talk, we cry, we laugh. She shares her poetry; I sing a gypsy song to her—our favorite. This is my legacy—what she has passed on to me—her need to write, to sing, to create…to survive.

Was it a dream? A hallucination? Psychic manifestation? I don't know. I know it happened and it seemed as real as this present moment.

It is beyond words, just feeling. Mama stands up, puts on her coat and hat. There is a long, warm embrace and then she is gone.

"До свиданье, Mourechka," I hear her say. (*Until next time.*)

PART EIGHT:

WHAT THE FUTURE HOLDS

My angers and frustrations have mellowed into contentment. Yet aspirations remain, inspiration rises. I know now that I can do anything I want, that new forms I run toward the rest of my life, open to embrace what new dreams I may have, fulfill all my artistic goals.

It is natural, then, that I write my first screenplay.

THE EXTRA

EXT.— EARLY EVENING (OVER TITLES)

A LONG shot of the ASTOR HOUSE MANSION in Rhinebeck, NY.

OVERLAY SOUND of heavy breathing, footsteps, grunts.

We see a slim very beautiful if older woman running as best she can up the beautiful tree-lined driveway toward the mansion. She is wearing a fancy dress, hat, and heels and carrying a pocketbook and several shopping bags. She carries dresses on hangers draped over her arms.

MARTHA stops for a moment to look at the elegant mansion then sees the line of porta potties.

Martha runs behind a tree, puts her things down, pulls her dress up. She is about to squat down to pee behind the tree when a security guard stops her and points to the Annex, a large, beautiful white manor house with a wraparound porch next to the mansion. Martha pulls her dress down, picks up her things, and walks toward the Annex.

She walks quickly past several trucks loaded with massive amounts of film equipment. Wires and lights are hanging everywhere, and we see more and more FILM CREW milling about shouting orders. Martha (amazed) at the scope of this project.

TITLES END

INT. GROUND FLOOR OF THE ANNEX BUILDING—EVENING

Martha (breathless) enters the ground floor of the Annex. A security guard stops her.

Martha starts rummaging through her pocketbook looking for ID. She cannot find her wallet and is frantically searching for some sort of ID. All sorts of things are coming out of her pocketbook and are dropping on the floor. Her dresses and shopping bags are lying on the floor. Martha (distraught) until she finally finds her NYC Senior Transit Bus Pass. Martha shows it to the security guard.

CLOSE UP: NYC SENIOR TRANSIT PASS WITH PHOTO ID.

The guard lets her through. Assistant appears.

ASSISTANT

Are you here for the film shoot?

MARTHA

(Russian accent)

Yes, yes. Am I too late?

ASSISTANT

No, no, you're right on time. Follow me.

Martha schlepps her baggage and follows the young girl. They pass an indoor tennis court, indoor swimming pool, formal rooms with high ceilings, chandeliers, and floor-to-ceiling windows.

INT. WAITING ROOM OF THE ANNEX— EVENING

The huge garage space is hot and stuffy and teeming with FILM CREW, ACTORS, EXTRAS who are talking—men, women, children of all different ages are dressed in an assortment of costumes—evening gowns, tuxedos, boas. It is noisy. Some people are milling about, getting dressed, putting on makeup. Some are sitting and waiting.

<u>Camera notes</u>: DO NOT TOUCH signs are plastered over a pile of furniture behind the large room.

ASSISTANT

Let me see what you brought.

Martha lays out her outfits and pulls costume jewelry and accessories from her shopping bags and puts them on the designated table.

ASSISTANT

(picking out one outfit from the pile).

Nice dresses.

MARTHA

Dance costumes. I'm a dancer—

ASSISTANT

(cuts Martha off)

Lovely. Why don't you put this on for the first scene. The makeup lady will come around and make you up.

ASSISTANT exits.

INT. ANNEX— NINE P.M.

Martha walks inside the corridors of the Annex, peeking into rooms. She sees the VIP room with a table laden with delicious food—fresh fruit, bread, plates of meat and cheese. There's a VERBOTEN sign above the door. She looks down at the open potato chip bag in her pocketbook and stuffs it back into her bag. She continues down a corridor where she sees a sign for a toilet. She is about to open the door to the toilet when a security guard blocks her way.

SECURITY GUARD points his finger in the direction of the porta potties.

MARTHA

I cannot. Please...

Martha stands in front of the guard with her legs crossed, unable to move.

Security guard looks around to see if anyone is looking and nods his head for Martha to go in.

INT. THE WAITING ROOM—TEN P.M.

Martha reenters the waiting room dressed in an off-the-shoulder red velvet dress with a white silk scarf wrapped around her neck. She is made up and is wearing high-heeled shoes.

It is hot in the garage. Martha is fanning herself with a paper plate. Fresh makeup is dripping off her face as she is blotting the sweat. Her velvet dress begins to melt, and she flips the back of her dress over the chair, leaving her sitting in her underwear. She finds her flip-flops in the shopping bag and puts them on. She drinks from her water bottle. Drains it.

EXT. MAIN ENTRANCE OF THE ANNEX—MIDNIGHT

Martha is among a group of EXTRAS who are being herded up the stairs by the Assistant. The EXTRAS are placed at the entrance of the Annex. Martha takes her position in the front.

ASSISTANT

> Ladies and Gentlemen. This is a German film called *The Second Time Around*; it's a big-budget film; you are to be guests in this mansion. You are now at the foyer. There will be a dance in the house later but for now I want you to move around slowly, sip the champagne, and make small talk. Cars will be coming up the candlelit driveway and we want you to greet the guests. Everyone ready? Good. TAKE ONE. ACTION.

Shiny, luxurious cars pull up to the entrance of the Annex, letting well-dressed, gowned passengers out. The gas torches are lit, movie cameras rolling. Extras in servant outfits are running around filling the guests' glasses with sparkling cider, a stand-in for champagne.

Martha sashays through the group of EXTRAS, flaunting her beautiful dress and making sure she is in the shooting frame. Martha notices other EXTRAS standing on a red carpet and she pushes her way forward to make sure she is in the frame in front of them.

Martha stands on the red carpet with her fake champagne and IMAGINES herself being interviewed.

INSERT: A SHORT FILM CLIP of

Martha being interviewed at the Oscars. She is standing on the red carpet and an interviewer at the Oscars is speaking with her.

ASSISTANT

CUT…

CAMERA CLOSES on Christian Leipzig, who is walking toward the EXTRAS. He is the German film director—tall and handsome with long hair tied back in a ponytail. He is a striking figure in his blue jeans and tight white T-shirt. He walks up to Martha, who is still standing on the carpet, daydreaming.

`DIRECTOR

(with an elegant, sexy German accent).

Hello. What is your name?

MARTHA

(noticing who she is speaking with).

Marta. (excited) *Wie geht es Ihnen? Ich Spreche Deutshe*. I'm really Russian… Perhaps you heard of my family? The Meyendorffs? Baron Meyendorff? I could call myself Baronessa Meyendorff, but people would not understand. We have German ancestry way back. Maybe that saved us during the war. As Russians, we were doomed…

INSERT: NEWS CLIPS

Archival 1917 news clips of Bolsheviks and the Imperial Cossacks cutting people down on the streets of St. Petersburg, Russia. Clip of Winter Palace being stormed. Russian tsarist flag. Clips of refugees, men, women, and children, running to board a ship. Clips of refugees with tags in their lapels arriving in NYC circa 1950s. Mother, father, child passport photos with German Nazi emblem.

DIRECTOR (V.O. the last of the clips)

(cuts her off)

Yes, yes, thank you. I am very happy that you are here, Baronessa Meyendorff...BUT your dress is too bright. I can't seem to keep you out of the frame. Why don't you go upstairs and prepare yourself for the dancing scene in the ballroom. I think your dress will work better there.

DIRECTOR turns and leaves.

OTHER EXTRA

(to Martha)

Well, well, if it isn't the baroness. That's what you get for trying to shove your way up front.

INT. BALLROOM—ONE A.M.

A luxurious front room with an enormous fireplace, an exquisite chandelier, polished wood floors, and floor-to-ceiling windows with hanging lace curtains. A grand piano stands in the corner.

Martha enters.

ASSISTANT

Please find a partner and start waltzing on ACTION. If you don't know how to waltz, stand against the wall and let someone else dance.

There is a quick flurry of excitement as the EXTRAS look for partners. People are reaching over each other, calling out names. Martha is quick to grab a YOUNG MAN who is standing in front of her and begins to waltz with her partner.

WE see MARTHA regarding him as a nerd; she rolls her eyes.

INSERT: FILM CLIPS of

A beautiful mansion in Russia, early 1900s. A ballroom—guests are swirling around, waltzing to a full orchestra...

MARTHA

(V.O. film clips)

My name is Martha and I'm a Russian Baronessa, a dancer, and an actress. My family lived in an elegant mansion in Russia. Of course, they lost everything after WWII, so we lived in poverty when we immigrated to America. I had a very successful acting and dancing career. There has not been much work lately.

They whirl toward the camera. Martha points to the piano, where the camera is, and motions to the young man to go faster. YOUNG MAN is trying to maintain his composure, dabbing his sweaty forehead with a handkerchief. Then a flamboyant turn, Martha's sweaty hand slips out of the YOUNG MAN'S and Martha spins out and away from him, sliding across the slippery polished wooden floor, and lands in a heap in the corner of the ballroom.

DIRECTOR

CUT! What is happening here? Somebody please help the lady on the floor. OK, everyone back downstairs.

YOUNG MAN comes over to Martha and lends her his arm to help her up. He pours her sparkling apple cider into a champagne glass and gives it to her. She sips; she makes a face from the disgusting taste. She slowly gets up.

Martha and the young man exit the ballroom. She leans on his arm.

INT. WAITING ROOM—TWO A.M.

Martha (exhausted) is sitting and rubbing her thigh after her fall. YOUNG MAN sits next to her.

ASSISTANT enters.

ASSISTANT

> Martha? You are being asked by the director to do a scene with the leads. Change into another one of your costumes, go to the VIP room, and wait for the makeup lady to freshen your makeup up there. We will call for you.

ASSISTANT exits

Martha comes alive, picks out an outfit, grabs her pocketbook and shopping bag with her cosmetics and shoes. She gives the YOUNG MAN *I told you so* look and exits.

INT VIP ROOM—TWO THIRTY A.M.

The VIP room is a beautiful large parlor room with several mirrors and a huge table laden with a lavish buffet.

Martha, dressed in another beautiful costume, is at the buffet table, piling food on a plate quickly. She sits down at a large table and begins to stuff the food down, chewing and smiling to herself. She takes out the potato chips and pretzels she has in her purse and throws them across the room into the garbage.

The ASSISTANT enters, catches Martha in mid-chew, and beckons Martha to follow her. Martha takes her plate with leftover food and puts it in her shopping bag.

EXT. THE ANNEX WRAP-AROUND PORCH— THREE A.M.

Martha climbs the stairs and stands on the porch facing the two young leads of the film. The attractive DIRECTOR meets them.

DIRECTOR

> Marta. Baronessa. Good to see you again. Have you recovered from your fall in the ballroom? I have chosen you because you have an interesting face, and you look very

elegant in your outfits. I need a distraction from the couple in the background.

DIRECTOR, CONT'D

Here is the scene. The two young lovers are sitting at the high table on the porch, drinking and talking. I want you to walk IN FRONT of them, with your drink in hand, until you get to the table on the other side of the porch. You will stop at the table and continue drinking. Understand?

MARTHA

Did you know of the Meyendorff family? I was born in a refugee camp in Germany. I had to survive—

DIRECTOR

Sorry, Baronessa. I have to finish this shot now. Ready? PLACES. ACTION!

Martha begins to walk. As she is crossing the stage, she is fantasizing being a DIVA center stage.

INSERT: A PHOTO COLLAGE of Martha acting in various plays, taking curtain calls, her name in lights on the marquee.

V.O. PHOTO COLLAGE:

A series of about 6-7 CUT and ACTION calls.

Martha has to start her walk across the stage over and over. She is beginning to unravel; her walk is faltering.

ASSISTANT

> I'm sorry. I know it's about four a.m., but we have to get this scene right. One more take...ACTION

Martha starts to walk again and gets to the center of the room and she stops. Her legs are crossed, and she cannot move. She begins to laugh hysterically.

A small puddle is forming at her feet. Staff is running toward Martha to find out what happened while Martha discreetly tips her glass and spills apple cider onto the floor to camouflage the pee.

DIRECTOR

CUT!

EXT. OF THE ANNEX HOUSE—DAWN

A LONG SHOT of MARTHA walking with difficulty, weighted down with all of her stuff. She is walking away from the Annex. She is still dressed in a beautiful dress and in heels. She is walking alone with her shopping bags and dresses.

CLOSE UP of MARTHA'S face as tears roll down her cheeks, streaking the mascara.

MARTHA stops and looks at the money she's holding in her hand. She counts the money.

CLOSE UP: We see the money—three twenties, a ten, and a five-dollar bill.

MARTHA throws the money into the air. The bills flutter like leaves in the dawn breeze. She allows the tears to stream down her cheeks.

We see Martha (slowly) turn toward the ASTOR HOUSE MANSION, stop, then start walking again. As she walks, we see Martha transform.

We see Martha is a YOUNG BEAUTIFUL GIRL (can be imagined to be the young MARTHA).

CAMERA PULLS BACK SLOWLY to A LONG shot of the ASTOR HOUSE MANSION. We see YOUNG MARTHA running across a luscious green meadow, graceful and lithe toward the rising sun.

FIN

ACKNOWLEDGEMENTS

There were many times in my life when I found it difficult to accept being a Russian émigré in America. In the 1950's, I participated in the elementary school "under the desk duck and cover" drills because Cold War fears focused on possible Russian invasion. Then again, through the 1960's Vietnam War when the Viet Cong were viewed as the enemy and Russians in America were often called "commies." As a teenager who protested the war, "commie" was hard to take and for several years, I stopped speaking Russian. As a young adult, I had to break free of the Chekhovian impoverished émigré existence my parents led in Nyack, New York. At that time, I saw my departure as an escape from all they represented.

Now as I reflect on my past, I realize how interesting my life has been as a Russian American and how much value I absorbed from that culture. For this, I thank my parents, the Baron and Baronessa

Meyendorff who brought me up with Russian traditions and the rich Russian legacy of literature, music, art, dance and theatre; they made me attend Russian school on Saturdays to read, write and speak Russian so I would never forget. From my parents, I also inherited the creativity and artistry that allowed me to open doors into my many professions, teaching and performing.

I wish they could see me now.

I thank my husband and soulmate, Miklos Rudnay (Miky), for being my rock, my strength when I needed it; for cooking Hungarian comfort food when I was busy writing; for picking me up off the floor after a computer glitch meltdown and finally for his never-ending patience and unconditional love.

I extend my gratitude to Ed McCann, Sigrid Heath and Eva Tenuto for giving me the opportunity to perform my writing; to bring the stories from the page to the stage.

I'm appreciative of Amy Knupp for doing an extraordinary job of proofreading.

And I thank Jace for a gorgeous book cover design and holding my hand as I navigated the digitalized world, the final steps to publication.

Made in the USA
Middletown, DE
16 February 2021